Seguin's
COMPUTER Applications

with Microsoft® Office 2016

Second Edition

Workbook

Denise Seguin
Fanshawe College, London, Ontario

PARADIGM
EDUCATION SOLUTIONS

St. Paul

Senior Vice President	Linda Hein
Editor in Chief	Christine Hurney
Senior Editor	Cheryl Drivdahl
Developmental Editor, Digital and Print	Tamborah Moore
Assistant Developmental Editors	Mamie Clark and Katie Werdick
Contributing Writer	Janet Blum
Tester	Jeff Johnson
Director of Production	Timothy W. Larson
Production Editors	Rachel Kats and Carrie Rogers
Cover and Text Designer, Senior Production Specialist	Jaana Bykonich
Copy Editor	Heidi Hogg
Indexer	Terry Casey
Vice President Sales and Marketing	Scott Burns
Director of Marketing	Lara Weber McLellan
Vice President Information Technology	Chuck Bratton
Digital Projects Manager	Tom Modl
Digital Learning Manager	Troy Weets
Digital Production Manager	Aaron Esnough
Senior Digital Production Specialist	Julie Johnston
Web Developer	Blue Earth Interactive
Video Producer	Hurix Systems

ISBN 978-0-76387-189-5 (print)
ISBN 978-0-76386-888-8 (digital)

© 2017 by Paradigm Publishing, Inc.
875 Montreal Way
St. Paul, MN 55102
Email: educate@emcp.com
Website: www.emcp.com

Contents

Seguin COMPUTER Applications with Microsoft Office 2016

Study Tools

Study tools, including a slide presentation and Quick Steps, are available from this ebook page.

Review Exercises

Multiple Choice, Matching, and Completion exercises give you an opportunity to review and reinforce your understanding of the material covered in this chapter.

SNAP If you are a SNAP user, go to your SNAP Assignments page to complete the review exercises.

SNAP Exercises

SNAP If you are a SNAP user, go to your SNAP Assignments page to complete additional exercises available for you.

Assessments

The following assessments offer opportunities to apply what you have learned in relevant, real-world situations. Save your solution files and URLs, and submit them for evaluation as directed by your instructor.

Assessment 1.1 Exploring Windows 10 Apps

Type: Individual
Deliverable: Screen capture of desktop with Task View thumbnails

1. Start Windows 10 and sign in.
2. Start the News app. Scroll through the list of stories and then click the link to a story that interests you.
3. Start the Weather app and view the current weather forecast.
4. Start the Store app. Click the link to display the Games category. Click the link to a free game that interests you and then click the More link to read the game description.
5. Display Task View.
6. Press the Print Screen key on the keyboard to capture an image of your screen with Task View active. The key may be labeled Prt Sc, PrtScrn, or PrtSc and is generally located in the top row of keys at the right near the last function key. On some PCs or devices you may need to press Shift + Print Screen or a function key with Print Screen. If you are using a tablet without a keyboard, such as the Microsoft Surface Pro tablet, you can take a screen capture by holding down the Windows key and pressing the Volume Down button. If necessary, check with your instructor for instructions on how to submit assessments with screen capture deliverables.
7. Use the search text box to search for and launch the Paint application.
8. Click the Paste button on the Paint Home tab or insert the screen capture by opening the screen capture if you used some other method than those described in Step 6.

9. Click the Save button on the Quick Access Toolbar at the top of the Paint window. At the Save As dialog box, navigate to your USB flash drive in the left pane, select the current file name in the *File name* text box, type TaskView-YourName, and then click the Save button. (You will move this file to another location in Assessment 1.4.)
10. Close the Paint window.
11. Switch to and then close each of the three apps you started in this assessment.
12. Submit the assessment to your instructor in the manner she or he has requested.

Assessment 1.2 Customizing the Start Menu and Desktop

Type: Individual
Deliverable: Screen capture with customized Start menu shown on desktop

Note: Skip steps in this assessment that ask you to customize a tile if the tile is already at the instructed setting.

1. At the desktop, display the Start menu and then resize the Mail tile smaller.
2. Resize the Photos tile to Large.
3. Resize the Microsoft Edge tile to Medium.
4. Turn the live tile feature off the Calendar tile.
5. Turn the live tile feature off the Mail tile.
6. Rearrange the Mail, Photos, Microsoft Edge, and Calendar tiles to the top left of the right pane in an arrangement that suits you.
7. Resize the Start menu wider and taller than the current menu size.
8. Change the background image for the desktop to another image of your preference.
9. Change the accent color to another color of your preference and then close the Settings app window.
10. Display the Start menu and then capture an image of your customized Start menu and desktop. Paste the image into a new Paint window. See Assessment 1.1, Steps 6 to 8 if you need help.
11. Save the image in Paint on your USB flash drive as **Personalization-YourName**.
12. Close the Paint window.
13. Submit the assessment to your instructor in the manner she or he has requested.
14. Repeat Steps 1 to 9 restoring the tiles, Start menu, background, and accent color to their original settings and rearrange the tiles back to their original locations.

Assessment 1.3 Browsing Files with File Explorer

Type: Individual
Deliverable: Screen capture with File Explorer window

1. Start File Explorer.
2. If necessary, insert your USB flash drive into an empty USB port. If a new Removable Disk window opens, close the window.
3. At the File Explorer window, display in the Content pane the Removable Disk for your USB flash drive.
4. Navigate the following folders: ComputerCourse, CompletedTopicsByChapter, Ch1.
5. With the Ch1 files displayed in the Content pane, change the View to Large Icons.
6. Capture an image of the desktop with the File Explorer window open and paste it into a Paint window.
7. Save the image in Paint on your USB flash drive as **FileExplorerWindow-YourName**.
8. Close the Paint window and then close the File Explorer window.
9. Submit the assessment to your instructor in the manner she or he has requested.

◆ Data File   Assessment 1.4 Performing File Management Tasks

Type: Individual

Deliverable: Screen capture with File Explorer window

1. Start File Explorer and display in the Content pane the Assessments folder on your USB flash drive.
2. Create a new folder named *Ch1*.
3. Display the Student_Data_Files folder and then copy the Ch1 folder to the ComputerCourse folder.
4. Display in the Content pane the Ch1 folder within the ComputerCourse folder.
5. Select all files within the folder and move them to the Ch1 folder within Assessments.
6. With the Content pane displaying the files in the Ch1 folder within Assessments, do the following:
   a. Delete the files named **Fireworks**, **Winter**, and **PaintingBunting**.
   b. Rename the file **MurresOnIce** to *BirdsOnIceFloe*.
   c. Rename the file **BMMF** to *DrumsSolo*.
   d. Create a new folder named *NASA*.
   e. Select and move the following files to the NASA folder: **Apollo11Parade**, **ApolloLanding1966**, **ArmstrongMoon1969**, and **NASA_SpaceXFlight**.
   f. If necessary, change the View to List view.
7. Capture an image of the desktop with the File Explorer window showing the Content pane for the Ch1 folder within Assessments and paste it into a Paint window.
8. Save the image in Paint on your USB flash drive as **Ch1FileExplorer-YourName**.
9. Close the Paint window.
10. Display in the Content pane the ComputerCourse folder and then delete the folders *Ch1* and *Student_Data_Files*. (Note that another copy of the folder Student_Data_Files is on the USB flash drive.)
11. Create a new folder *ScreenCaptures* within the Ch1 folder in Assessments and then move all the Paint files created with screen captures to the new folder.
12. Close the File Explorer window.
13. Submit the assessment (from Step 8) to your instructor in the manner she or he has requested.

Assessment 1.5 Planning a New Folder Structure

Type: Individual

Deliverable: Document with recommended folder structure

1. Assume that you volunteer at the local animal rescue organization. You have been asked by the board of directors to organize the files stored on the computer in the office. In looking through the Documents folder in File Explorer, you discover that all the files have been saved to the Documents folder without any structure. In looking through the folder, you determine the following types of files are present:
   - photographs of cats, dogs, horses, and other animals that have been rescued
   - reports and invoices from veterinarians who attended to rescued animals
   - contact information for donors
   - budget and donor financial worksheets
   - applications from adoption families
   - minutes of board meetings
   - fund raising activities
   - supplies lists
   - animal pharmaceuticals
   - individual rescue animal records including adoptee information

2. Create a plan for a folder structure that will allow you to organize the Documents folder so that related files are grouped in a logical manner.
3. Start WordPad (find WordPad using the search text box) and create a document that explains your planned folder structure for the animal rescue charity.
4. Click the Save button on the Quick Access Toolbar at the top of the WordPad window. At the Save As dialog box, navigate to the Ch1 folder in Assessments on your USB flash drive, type the file name AnimalRescueFolders-YourName, and then click the Save button.
5. Close the WordPad window.
6. Submit the assessment to your instructor in the manner she or he has requested.

Assessment 1.6 Learning Windows 10

Type: Individual
Deliverable: Document about Windows 10 feature

1. Open the Get started app.
2. Click a category to a topic that interests you in the left pane.
3. Read about the feature in the right pane and if necessary, click tiles or links to additional content about the feature so that you understand how the feature works.
4. Start Wordpad (find WordPad using the search text box) and type in a new document screen the main points that you learned about the feature or other topic using your own words.
5. Save the WordPad document as **GetStarted-YourName** in the Ch1 folder in Assessments on your USB flash drive.
6. Close the WordPad window.
7. Submit the assessment to your instructor in the manner she or he has requested.
8. Eject the USB flash drive and then sign out of Windows.

Study Tools

Study tools, including a slide presentation and Quick Steps, are available from this ebook page.

Review Exercises

Multiple Choice, Matching, and Completion exercises give you an opportunity to review and reinforce your understanding of the material covered in this chapter.

If you are a SNAP user, go to your SNAP Assignments page to complete the review exercises.

SNAP Exercises

If you are a SNAP user, go to your SNAP Assignments page to complete additional exercises available for you.

Assessments

The following assessments offer opportunities to apply what you have learned in relevant, real-world situations. Save your solution files and URLs, and submit them for evaluation as directed by your instructor.

Assessment 2.1 Browsing Web Pages

Type: Individual
Deliverable: Screen captures of web pages or PDF documents of web pages

1. Start Microsoft Edge, Chrome, or Firefox and navigate to www.nga.gov, which is the web page for the National Gallery of Art in Washington, DC.
2. Navigate to the Exhibitions page and then click the link to a current exhibition of your choosing.
3. Add the page to Favorites (Microsoft Edge) or bookmark the page (Chrome or Firefox).
4. Do *one* of the following tasks (check with your instructor for his or her preferred output method):
   a. Save a screen capture of the web page you visited in a file named **WebBrowsing1–YourName** in a new folder Ch2 created within the Assessments folder on your storage medium.
   b. Select Microsoft Print to PDF as the Printer in the Print dialog box and then click Print. A PDF document is generated from the web page. At the Save Print Output As dialog box, save the PDF document as **WebBrowsing1–YourName** in a new folder Ch2 in the Assessments folder on your storage medium.
5. Open a new tab and navigate to www.navy.mil, the web page for the US Navy.
6. Add the page to Favorites (Microsoft Edge) or bookmark the page (Chrome or Firefox).
7. Navigate to one of the Navy News Service Top Stories.

8. Save a screen capture of the web page, or print to a PDF document. Use the same method you followed in Step 4 and name the new file **WebBrowsing2-YourName** in the Ch2 folder in Assessments.
9. Close the tab for the National Gallery of Art page.
10. Display the Favorites list (Microsoft Edge) in the Hub or the Bookmarks bar (Chrome or Firefox) and save a screen capture of the browser window in a file named **WebFavorites-YourName** in the Ch2 folder in Assessments.
11. Close Microsoft Edge, Chrome, or Firefox and any other programs that you opened.
12. Submit the assessment to your instructor in the manner she or he has requested.

Assessment 2.2 Searching for Information on the Web

Type: Individual
Deliverable: Document with search criteria and search results information

1. Start Microsoft Edge, Chrome, or Firefox.
2. Display the web page for your favorite search engine and search for information on resume writing tips.
3. Start a new WordPad document (find WordPad using the search text box) and record the following information:
   a. The search engine you used and the search phrase you typed to find information.
   b. The number of pages returned in the search results list. *Note: Some search engines show the number of results at the bottom of the first page.*
4. Next, return to the web browser and apply search options at the search engine website to help you narrow the search results. If necessary, use the Help feature for the search engine to learn how to specify advanced search options or use a different search engine that offers more options for narrowing a search.
5. Switch to the document window and type a description of the search options you applied and the number of pages returned in the new search results list.
6. Switch to the web browser, navigate to one of the links on the search results page, and read the information on resume writing tips. Select and copy the URL in the Address bar.
7. Switch to the document window, paste the URL of the page you visited below the search statistics, and add in your own words a brief summary of new information you learned by reading the web page.
8. Save the document as **ResumeSearch-YourName** in the Ch2 folder in Assessments.
9. Close the web browser and WordPad windows.
10. Submit the assessment to your instructor in the manner she or he has requested.

Assessment 2.3 Downloading Content from a Web Page

Type: Individual
Deliverable: Document with downloaded photograph of World War I soldiers

1. Start Microsoft Edge, Chrome, or Firefox and navigate to The Commons page at flickr.com.
2. Search The Commons for pictures of soldiers from World War I.
3. Select and download a picture to your computer.
4. Start a new WordPad document and paste the picture into the document. (Use the Picture button on the Home tab.)
5. Switch to the web browser, select and copy the URL for the photograph, and paste it below the picture in the document.

6. Save the document as **WWIPicture-YourName** in the Ch2 folder in Assessments.
7. Close the WordPad and web browser windows.
8. Submit the assessment to your instructor in the manner she or he has requested.

Assessment 2.4 Exploring a New Search Engine

Type: Individual or Pairs
Deliverable: Document with comparison information for two search engines

1. Start Microsoft Edge, Chrome, or Firefox, navigate to your favorite search engine web page, and search for information on job interview techniques. Apply advanced search options to try to narrow the search results as much as possible to high-quality information about job interviews.
2. Next, conduct a search using the phrase "top five popular search engines."
3. Read at least one article in the search results. Choose a search engine from the article you read that you do not normally use. If you are doing this assessment in pairs, each person selects a different search engine.
4. Navigate to the new search engine you selected and conduct a search on job interview techniques. Use the same search phrase at each search engine.
5. Compare the search results from each search engine. Was the number of pages in the search results close to the same number? On page one of search results at each search engine, how many web pages were repeated and how many web pages were different? Did one search engine seem to return more targeted results? Do you think you will use the new search engine in the future, or will you revert to the one you favored before?
6. Create a WordPad document with answers to the questions and, for the last question, provide your reasons. Include the two search engines and the search phrase you used to complete this assessment.
7. Save the document as **SearchEngineComparison-YourName** in the Ch2 folder in Assessments.
8. Close the WordPad and web browser windows.
9. Submit the assessment to your instructor in the manner she or he has requested.

Assessment 2.5 Exploring Creative Commons Content

Type: Individual or Pairs
Deliverable: Document with information on creative commons licenses and content

1. Start Microsoft Edge, Chrome, or Firefox and navigate to creativecommons.org.
2. Click <u>About</u>, click <u>About CC</u> and then read the page that describes the creative commons assessment.
3. Next, use your favorite search engine to find a picture of a well known landmark in your geographic area available under a creative commons license.
4. Download a copy of the picture and insert the picture into a WordPad document. Copy and paste the URL for the picture below the photograph.
5. Add a brief summary in your own words below the picture of the main points from the About CC page.
6. Save the document as **CreativeCommons-YourName** in the Ch2 folder in Assessments.
7. Close the WordPad and web browser windows.
8. Submit the assessment to your instructor in the manner she or he has requested.

Study Tools

 **Study Tools**

Study tools, including a slide presentation and Quick Steps, are available from this ebook page.

Review Exercises

 **Review Exercises**

Multiple Choice, Matching, and Completion exercises give you an opportunity to review and reinforce your understanding of the material covered in this chapter.

 **SNAP**

If you are a SNAP user, go to your SNAP Assignments page to complete the review exercises.

SNAP Exercises

SNAP

If you are a SNAP user, go to your SNAP Assignments page to complete additional exercises available for you.

Assessments

The following assessments offer opportunities to apply what you have learned in relevant, real-world situations. Save your solution files and URLs, and submit them for evaluation as directed by your instructor.

 **Data Files**

Assessment 3.1 Start a New Presentation and Copy Object to Slide from Excel

Type: Individual
Deliverable: PowerPoint Presentation

1. Start Excel 2016 and then open the student data file named **CutRateRentals**.
2. Start a new blank presentation in PowerPoint 2016.
3. Type CutRate Car Rentals as the slide title text.
4. Click the Layout button in the Slides group on the Home tab and then click *Title Only* to change the slide layout.
5. Select the title text, apply bold and italic formatting, change the color of the text to a color of your choice, and then deselect the text.
6. Switch to Excel, select and copy the pie chart, switch to PowerPoint, and then paste the chart on the slide.
7. Save the presentation as **CutRateRentals-YourName** in a new folder named Ch3 in the Assessments folder on your storage medium.
8. Close PowerPoint and then close Excel.
9. Submit the assessment to your instructor in the manner she or he has requested.

Assessment 3.2 Modify a Presentation and Copy Content to Word

Type: Individual
Deliverable: Word Document and PDF Document

1. Start PowerPoint and then open the **CutRateRentals-YourName** presentation.

2. Use Save As to save a copy of the file in the same location as **CutRateRentalsRevised–YourName**.
3. Select and resize the chart using a corner selection handle so the chart fills most of the slide below the title.
4. With the chart still selected, move it as needed so that it is centered below the title using the alignment guides to assist you with the move. ***Hint:*** *Do not drag to move the chart while the mouse is positioned over a pie slice.*
5. With the chart still selected, use the Change Colors gallery in the Chart Styles group on the Chart Tools Design tab to change the color scheme for the pie chart to another color of your choosing.
6. With the chart still selected, use the Shape Styles gallery on the Chart Tools Format tab to apply a shape style option of your choosing. ***Hint:*** *Click the More button (bottom button that displays with a bar and down-pointing arrow below it at the right end of the gallery) to view more options in a drop-down grid.*
7. Save the revised presentation using the same name.
8. Start a new blank document in Word 2016.
9. Copy the slide title text from the PowerPoint presentation and paste the text into the Word document. After the text is pasted, use the Paste Options button to apply the *Keep Source Formatting* option.
10. Press Enter to create a new blank line after the title text.
11. Copy the chart from the PowerPoint presentation and paste it below the title in the Word document.
12. Save the Word document as **CutRateRentals–YourName** in the Ch3 folder in Assessments on your storage medium.
13. Export the Word document as a PDF with the same name and saved in the same location.
14. If a window opens with the PDF document in it, close the window.
15. Close Word and then close PowerPoint.
16. Submit the assessment to your instructor in the manner she or he has requested.

Assessment 3.3 👁 Visual—Create a Florida Vacation Flyer

Type: Individual or Pairs
Deliverable: Flyer as document or PDF

1. Research a Florida destination that you would like to travel to during the next school break, including the approximate cost for one week. Include in the cost estimate travel, lodging, food, visitor attractions, and souvenirs.
2. Make a list of 5 to 10 points to include in the flyer based on the research you conducted. For example, provide a list of tourist attractions or events that make the destination inviting.
3. Create a flyer in Word named **FloridaFlyer–YourName** similar to the Assessment 3.3 Florida Vacation Flyer shown on the next page, and save it in the Ch3 folder in Assessments on your storage medium. Substitute information from your research in place of the example text. Use your best judgment to determine formatting options to apply to the text. Apply the following options to the picture: +40% Brightness and Contrast correction, width of 2.5 inches, Top and Bottom Text Wrapping, and Reflected Rounded Rectangle Picture Style.
4. Export the flyer as a PDF with the same name and saved in the same location and then close Word.
5. Submit the assessment to your instructor in the manner she or he has requested.

◆ **View**
Model Answer
Compare your
completed file with
the model answer.

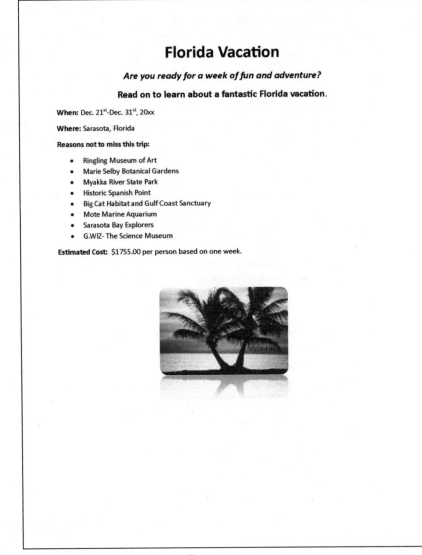

Assessment 3.3 Florida Vacation Flyer

Assessment 3.4 Use Tell Me to Find Help on a PowerPoint Feature

Type: Individual
Deliverable: PowerPoint Presentation

1. Start PowerPoint 2016 and then open the file **CutRateRentals–YourName** created in Assessment 3.1.
2. Use Save As to save a copy of the file in the same location as **CutRateRentalsBar–YourName**.
3. Use the Tell Me feature to help you change the chart from a 3D pie chart to a 3D bar chart.
4. Resize the bar chart so that it fills up as much of the slide as possible below the title.
5. Save the revised presentation using the same name.
6. Submit the assessment to your instructor in the manner she or he has requested.

Study Tools

Study tools, including a slide presentation and Quick Steps, are available from this ebook page.

Review Exercises

Multiple Choice, Matching, and Completion exercises give you an opportunity to review and reinforce your understanding of the material covered in this chapter.

If you are a SNAP user, go to your SNAP Assignments page to complete the review exercises.

SNAP Exercises

If you are a SNAP user, go to your SNAP Assignments page to complete additional exercises available for you.

Assessments

The following assessments offer opportunities to apply what you have learned in relevant, real-world situations. Save your solution files and URLs, and submit them for evaluation as directed by your instructor.

Assessment 4.1 Start a New Notebook and Create Notebook Structure

Type: Individual
Deliverable: OneNote Notebook (continued in Assessment 4.2)

1. Create a new folder named *Ch4* in the Assessments folder on your storage medium.
2. Start OneNote 2016 and display the New Notebook backstage area. Create a new notebook as follows:
   a. Use the *Browse* option to create the new notebook in the Ch4 folder in Assessments on your storage medium.
   b. Name the new notebook **NotebookPractice-YourName**.
3. Rename the New Section 1 section tab *Computer Research* and add the page title *Images*.
4. Add a new section titled *Law Course* with a page titled *Current Topics in Law*.
5. Add a new section titled *Tourism Course* with a page titled *Presentations*.
6. Add a new section titled *Volunteer Work* with a page titled *Medical Clinic Association Conference*.
7. Leave the notebook open if you are continuing on to Assessment 4.2; otherwise, close the notebook and submit the notebook to your instructor in the manner she or he has requested.

**Data Files**   **Assessment 4.2** Adding Notes and External Content to a Notebook

Type: Individual

Deliverable: OneNote Notebook (continued from Assessment 4.1 and continues in Assessment 4.3)

1. If necessary, open the notebook created in Assessment 4.1.
2. Embed a copy of the contents in the Excel file **MedClinicsFees** on the Medical Clinic Association Conference page in the *Volunteer Work* section.
3. Embed a copy of the PowerPoint presentation **WaikikiPres** on the Presentations page in the *Tourism Course* section.
4. Insert the Word document **FamilyAndLawAssgnt** as an icon on the Current Topics in Law page in the *Law Course* section and type Assignment 1 due in week 5 as note text below the icon.
5. Insert the image file **IBMCptr_1961** on the Images page in the *Computer Research* section and type IBM computer from 1961 as note text below the photograph.
6. Add a new page to the *Computer Research* section with the page title *History of Computers* and add a hyperlink to the web address www.computerhistory.org/timeline. Type The Timeline of Computer History from the Computer History Museum provides the history of computing starting in 1933 and continuing to present day..
7. Leave the notebook open if you are continuing on to Assessment 4.3; otherwise, close the notebook and submit the notebook to your instructor in the manner she or he has requested.

Assessment 4.3 Tagging Notes and Adding a Copy of a Web Page

Type: Individual

Deliverable: OneNote Notebook or PDF of Exported Notebook (continued from Assessments 4.1 and 4.2)

1. If necessary, open the notebook created in Assessments 4.1 and 4.2.
2. Assign the To Do tag at the beginning of the note text below the Word document icon on the Current Topics in Law page in the *Law Course* section.
3. Type This is included in test 1 in a new note at the top of the PowerPoint slides embedded on the Presentations page in the *Tourism Course* section and assign the Important tag to the note.
4. Open a browser window and search for a recent article about 3-D printing technology. Use the Take screen clipping tool to capture and copy the title and the first few paragraphs of an article that you find to a new page in the *Computer Research* section titled *3-D Printing*. Type Article for project 1 in a new note above the embedded content and assign the note the Important tag.
5. Click the File tab and then click *Export*. Click *Notebook* in the *1. Export Current* section and *PDF (*.pdf)* in the *2. Select Format* section at the Export backstage area. Click the Export button. At the Save As dialog box, navigate to the Ch4 folder in Assessments on your storage medium and accept the default file name for the PDF.
6. Close the notebook.
7. Submit the OneNote notebook or PDF file to your instructor in the manner she or he has requested.

Assessment 4.4 Creating a Notebook Repository for Assessments

Type: Individual

Deliverable: Shared Notebook on OneDrive

Note: Check with your instructor for his or her Microsoft account email address for Step 7 or for alternative instructions if he or she prefers that you create the MyAssessments notebook on your storage medium and not share the notebook.

1. Create a new notebook stored in your OneDrive account with the name **MyAssessments-YourName**. Click Not now when asked if you want to invite people to share the notebook.

2. Rename the New Section 1 section tab *Windows* and add the page title *Chapter 1.*

3. Add the following sections and pages:

Sections	Pages
Internet	Chapter 2
Office	Chapter 3
OneNote	Chapter 4
Outlook	
Word	
Excel	
PowerPoint	
Access	
Integrating	
CloudTech	

4. Make the Chapter 1 page in the *Windows* section active and then embed a copy of the first assessment file that you completed for Chapter 1. Next, embed a copy of each remaining assessment file for Chapter 1, one below the other.

5. Make the Chapter 2 page in the *Internet* section active and repeat the process you completed at Step 4 to insert a copy of each assessment file that you completed for Chapter 2.

6. Make the Chapter 3 page in the *Office* section active and repeat the process you completed at Step 4 to embed a copy of each assessment file that you completed for Chapter 3.

7. Make the Chapter 4 page in the *OneNote* section active and embed a copy of the PDF file created for Assessment 4.3.

Note: If you receive an error message when OneNote attempts the File Printout command, open the file in the source application (such as Word or Adobe Reader) and then use the Print *command to print the file with* Send to OneNote 2016 *as the printer. At the Select Location in OneNote dialog box, expand the notebook and section list as needed to click the desired destination page and then click OK. If you experience other technical difficulties, perform the Send to OneNote steps in a computer lab at your school where you can ask for technical assistance.*

8. Share the notebook with your instructor, typing an appropriate message after entering your instructor's Microsoft account email address.

9. Close the notebook and then close OneNote.

Note: Closing the notebook may take a few moments while the changes are synced to OneDrive.

Assessment 4.5 Exporting a OneNote Notebook and Copying the OneNote Folder

Type: Individual

Deliverable: Exported PDF of TechnologyCourse notebook

Note: In Steps 4 to 7 you copy the OneNote notebook folder from the Ch4 folder in Student_Data_Files because OneNote does not have a Save As option to allow you to save a copy of the OneNote notebook in another location. Be aware that icons to linked documents or presentations are linked to the drive and folder from which the content was originally added.

1. Start OneNote and then open the TechnologyCourse notebook that you worked on in Topics 4.1 to 4.5 from the Ch4 folder in Student_Data_Files on your storage medium.
2. Click the File tab and then click *Export*. Click *Notebook* in the *1. Export Current* section and *PDF (*.pdf)* in the *2. Select Format* section at the Export backstage area. Click the Export button. At the Save As dialog box, navigate to the CompletedTopicsByChapter folder within ComputerCourse on your storage medium. Create a new folder *Ch4* within CompletedTopicsByChapter. Double-click to open the Ch4 folder. Click in the *File name* text box at the end of the existing file name, add **-YourName** to the end of the file name, and then click the Save button.
3. Close the notebook and then close OneNote.
4. Open a File Explorer window.
5. Navigate to the Ch4 folder in Student_Data_Files on your storage medium.
6. Select and copy the TechnologyCourse folder, and then paste the folder in the Ch4 folder within CompletedTopicsByChapter.
7. Close the File Explorer window.

Study Tools

Study tools, including a slide presentation and Quick Steps, are available from this ebook page.

Review Exercises

Multiple Choice, Matching, and Completion exercises give you an opportunity to review and reinforce your understanding of the material covered in this chapter.

SNAP If you are a SNAP user, go to your SNAP Assignments page to complete the review exercises.

SNAP Exercises

SNAP If you are a SNAP user, go to your SNAP Assignments page to complete additional exercises available for you.

Assessments

The following assessments offer opportunities to apply what you have learned in relevant, real-world situations. Save your solution files and URLs, and submit them for evaluation as directed by your instructor.

Data Files   **Assessment 5.1** Open an Outlook Data File and Add and Edit Items

Type: Individual
Deliverable: Updated Outlook Data File (continued in Assessment 5.2)

1. Create a new folder named *Ch5* in the Assessments folder on your storage medium.
2. Start Outlook 2016 and make sure the Folder pane and Reading pane are displayed with Inbox active.
3. Open an existing Outlook data file with Outlook items by completing the following steps:
   a. Click the File tab and then click *Open & Export*.
   b. Click the Open Outlook Data File option at the Open backstage area.
   c. At the Open Outlook Data File dialog box, navigate to the Ch5 folder in Student_Data_Files on your storage medium and then double-click the file **Ch5-OutlookPracticeData**. A new entry appears in the Folder pane below your current mail folders with the title *ch5-outlookpracticedata*.
4. Click the white right-pointing arrow next to **ch5-outlookpracticedata** in the Folder pane to expand the folder list. Click the black diagonal downward-pointing arrow next to your email address (or your Outlook user name) in the Folder pane to collapse the folder list. The Folder pane now should show only the mail folders in the new data file opened at Step 3.

Note: For the remaining steps in this assessment and the next assessment, complete all tasks using the folders in the expanded folder list for ch5-outlookpracticedata.

5. Make Inbox active to view the two messages and forward each message to yourself (use your email address) with the message text *Here is a copy of the message from (enter sender's name in the original message).*

6. Display all the other folders in the data file by clicking the More button (displays as ellipsis points, or three dots) on the Navigation pane and then clicking *Folders* at the pop-up list. If necessary, collapse again the list of folders for your regular email account.

7. Click Calendar in the Folder pane and display October 15, 2018 in the Appointment area. Make the following changes to appointments in the Calendar (respond *Yes* to any messages that appear about reminders):

   a. On Monday, October 15, add *Room A-109* as the location for the Project updates appointment.

   b. Change the lunch with Taylor Gorski from Tuesday, October 16 to Wednesday, October 17 at 1:00 p.m.

   c. Make the doctor appointment on Wednesday, October 17, 1.5 hours in duration.

   d. Change the Health and Safety Training on October 18 to Thursday, October 11 and make it a recurring appointment at the same day and time for three weeks.

8. Click Contacts in the Folder pane and make the following changes to the People list:

   a. Change the *Work* telephone number for Xavier Borman to *888-555-4523*.

   b. Change the *Title* for Taylor Gorski to *President & CEO*.

   c. Add a new person to the People list with the following contact information and add a picture using the file **LuisPhillips** in the Ch5 folder in Student_Data_Files:
      Luis Phillips, NewAge Advertising, Sales Representative, luis@emcp.net

9. Click *Tasks* in the Folder pane and make the following changes:

   a. Remove the task *Find volunteers to help at conference* from the To-Do List.

   b. Mark the task *Update project wiki pages* completed.

   c. Change the due date for the task *Research click marketing strategies* to October 22, 2018.

   d. Add the following new tasks:
      Compile report from volunteer survey
      Return equipment rented for conference

10. Leave Outlook open if you are continuing to Assessment 5.2; otherwise, right-click **ch5-outlookpracticedata** and then click *Close "Ch5-OutlookPracticeData"* at the shortcut menu. Close Outlook and submit the assessment to your instructor in the manner she or he has instructed.

Assessment 5.2 Sending Outlook Items to a OneNote Notebook and Creating a PDF

Type: Individual
Deliverable: Page in OneNote notebook and PDF with Outlook Items Completed in Assessment 5.1

Note: You must have completed Assessment 4.4 in Chapter 4 and Assessment 5.1 in this chapter before starting this assessment.

1. Start OneNote 2016 and open the MyAssessments notebook created in Chapter 4, Assessment 4.4. Make the Outlook section active and then enter *Chapter 5* as the page title.

2. Switch to Outlook and make Calendar active. Display October 15, 2018 in the Appointment area and send the calendar to your OneNote notebook by completing the following steps:
   a. Click the Month button in the Arrange group on the Home tab.
   b. Display the Print backstage area and change the Printer to *Send to OneNote 2016* (your list may show the printer as *Send to OneNote 16*).
   c. Click the Print button.
   d. Click the OneNote 2016 button on the taskbar.
   e. At the Select Location in OneNote dialog box, click the plus symbol to expand *Outlook* in the section list for the MyAssessments-YourName notebook, click the Chapter 5 page, and then click OK. The Calendar will be embedded on the Chapter 5 page in the MyAssessments notebook.
3. Switch to Outlook and display the Contacts folder. Send the People list to your OneNote notebook by completing steps similar to those in Steps 2b to 2e. Accept the default *Card Style* format for the print *Settings*.
4. Switch to Outlook and display the Tasks folder. Change the current view to Simple List. Send the To-Do List to your OneNote notebook by completing steps similar to those in Steps 2b to 2e.
5. Switch to Outlook and display Mail. Right-click *ch5-outlookpracticedata* in the Folder pane and then click *Close "Ch5-OutlookPracticeData"*.
6. Click the white right-pointing arrow next to your email address (or your Outlook user name) to expand the folder list.
7. Make Inbox active and click Send/Receive All Folders button if necessary to update the message list.
8. Open the first message window for the message you forwarded to yourself in Assessment 5.1, Step 5. Send a copy of the message to your OneNote notebook by completing steps similar to those in Steps 2b to 2e and then close the message window.
9. Switch to Outlook and repeat Step 8 for the second message you forwarded to yourself in Assessment 5.1, Step 5.
10. With OneNote open and the Chapter 5 page in the *Outlook* section active, display the Export backstage area. With *Page* selected by default in the *1. Export Current* section, select *PDF (*.pdf)* in the *2. Select Format* section and then click the Export button. Navigate to the Ch5 folder in Assessments on your storage medium. Select the current text in the *File name* text box, type C5-OutlookPractice-YourName, and then click the Save button.
11. Leave OneNote open if you are continuing to Assessment 5.3; otherwise, close the notebook and then close OneNote.
12. In Outlook, click Mail on the Navigation pane to restore the Folder pane to the default folder list that displays mail folders only.
13. Leave Outlook open if you are continuing to Assessment 5.3; otherwise, close Outlook and submit the assessment to your instructor in the manner she or he has requested.

Assessment 5.3 Organizing Your School Activities in Outlook

Type: Individual

Deliverable: Page in OneNote notebook and PDF with New Outlook Items

1. In OneNote, create a new page in the *Outlook* section with the title *Assessment 5.3*.
2. Switch to Outlook, make Calendar active, and make sure the current date is displayed. Create appointments for your class schedule for all the courses you are currently taking as recurring appointments in the calendar for the remainder of the current semester.
3. Add other appointments to your Outlook calendar for any other school activities that you want to attend. For example, add an appointment or event for any extracurricular school activity.
4. Make People active and add your teacher's contact information to the People list.
5. Make Tasks active and create in the To-Do List a task entry for each upcoming test, project, or assignment (including due dates) of which you are aware in each of the courses you are currently taking.
6. Send the calendar in Month view, the People list in Card Style, and the To-Do List to the Assessment 5.3 page in the *Outlook* section of your OneNote notebook.
7. Create a PDF of the Assessment 5.3 page in your OneNote notebook, saving the PDF in the Ch5 folder in the Assessments folder on your storage medium with the name **Assessment5.3–YourName**.
8. Close your MyAssessments notebook in OneNote and then close OneNote.
9. Close Outlook.
10. Submit the assessment to your instructor in the manner she or he has requested.

Study Tools

Study tools, including a slide presentation and Quick Steps, are available from this ebook page.

Review Exercises

Multiple Choice, Matching, and Completion exercises give you an opportunity to review and reinforce your understanding of the material covered in this chapter.

If you are a SNAP user, go to your SNAP Assignments page to complete the review exercises.

SNAP Exercises

If you are a SNAP user, go to your SNAP Assignments page to complete additional exercises available for you.

Assessments

The following assessments offer opportunities to apply what you have learned in relevant, real-world situations. Save your solution files and URLs, and submit them for evaluation as directed by your instructor.

Assessment 6.1 Creating and Editing a New Document

Type: Individual
Deliverable: Word document (continued in Assessment 6.2)

1. At a new blank document, type the following text, pressing Enter only where indicated.
   Social Media Popularity, Profitability, and Privacy [press Enter]
   Ninety-six percent of Americans and Canadians between the ages of 16 and 24 are Internet users. For most people, a majority of time spent on the Internet involves the use of social communication websites, such as Facebook. All ages prefer the convenience and accessibility of social media websites to connect with family, friends, and acquaintances. [press Enter]
   Social media websites, such as Facebook, make money using a traditional model of selling advertisements, such as banner and pop-up ads. Facebook games, such as Candy Crush Saga, also provide a source of income for Facebook. [press Enter]
   Users of social media websites such as Facebook need to be wary of privacy issues and security threats. The risk of identity theft, clickjacking, and phishing scams is rising due to the popularity of social media. Review privacy options and keep personal information that could identify you to a stranger to a minimum at each social network. Consider asking your family and friends not to tag you in pictures without your knowledge. [press Enter]
   Your Name [press Enter]
2. Save the document as **SocialMedia-YourName** in a new folder *Ch6* within the Assessments folder on your storage medium.

3. Edit the document as follows:
   a. In the first sentence change *16 and 24 are Internet users* to *10 and 34 are social media users*.
   b. In the second sentence change *social communication websites* to *social networking websites*.
   c. Add the following sentence to the end of the second paragraph.

      Revenue from mobile ads represented more than two-thirds of all Facebook advertising income in a recent year.
   d. Delete the last sentence in the first paragraph that begins with *All ages prefer*.
   e. Delete the second sentence in the second paragraph that begins with *Facebook games*.
   f. Move the last sentence in the third paragraph that begins with *Consider asking* to the beginning of the last paragraph (before the sentence that begins *Users of social media websites*).
   g. Type the following new paragraph after the third paragraph and before your name.

      When posting content at a social media website, be mindful not to violate copyright by copying pictures that belong to someone else. Look for a copyright symbol © or refer to terms of use before downloading content. Be careful also not to misrepresent or misuse a registered trademark of a company. Look for the ® or ™ symbol to identify a company's trademark.
   h. Replace all occurrences of *social media* with *social networking*. When finished, change *networking* in the title to *Networking*.
4. Complete a spelling and grammar check of the document.
5. Proofread the document carefully to make sure the document is error-free.
6. Save the revised document using the same name (**SocialMedia-YourName**).
7. Leave the document open if you are continuing to Assessment 6.2; otherwise, close the document and submit the assessment to your instructor in the manner she or he has requested.

Assessment 6.2 Editing and Formatting a Document

Type: Individual
Deliverable: Word document

Note: You must have completed Assessment 6.1 before starting this assessment.
1. If necessary, open **SocialMedia-YourName**.
2. Use Save As to change the file name to **SocialMediaFormatted-YourName**, saving in the same folder.
3. Type the following new paragraph and bulleted list between the second and third paragraphs.

   Facebook's $12.5 billion revenue from a recent year is segmented as follows:
   - 85 percent from ads (including mobile ads)
   - 14 percent from games (such as Candy Crush Saga)
   - 1 percent from other sources
4. Format the document as follows:
   a. Change the title to 12-point Verdana bold red font and center-aligned.
   b. Indent the first line of each paragraph.
   c. Justify the first two and the last two paragraphs.
   d. Select the entire document, change the line spacing to 1.5, and remove the space after paragraphs.
5. Depending on the method used to format a paragraph with a first line indent, the indent position for the last three paragraphs may be at 0.25 inch instead of the 0.5 inch in the first two paragraphs. This occurs because the bullet list formatting carries over to the paragraphs before and after. If necessary, change the first line indent position to 0.5 inch for the last three paragraphs by positioning the insertion point within the

paragraph, opening the Paragraph dialog box, and changing the value in the *By* text box in the *Indentation* section.

6. Save the revised document using the same name (**SocialMediaFormatted-YourName**).
7. Submit the assessment to your instructor in the manner she or he has requested.
8. Close the document.

Assessment 6.3 Formatting with Styles

Type: Individual
Deliverable: Word document

Note: You must have completed Assessment 6.1 before starting this assessment.

1. Open **SocialMedia-YourName**.
2. Use Save As to change the file name to **SocialMediaStyles-YourName**, saving in the same folder.
3. Apply the Heading 1 style to the document title.
4. Select all the text below the title except for your name at the bottom of the document and apply the Emphasis style.
5. Select your name at the bottom of the document and apply the Intense Reference style.
6. Change the Style Set to *Black & White (Classic)*.
7. Save the revised document using the same name (**SocialMediaStyles-YourName**).
8. Submit the assessment to your instructor in the manner she or he has requested.
9. Close the document.

Assessment 6.4 Creating an Invoice from a Template

Type: Individual
Deliverable: Invoice document from template

1. Search for and select a service invoice template of your choosing to create a new document. Note that you may need to modify the presentation of the information given at Step 3a to match the template you select. For example, not all service invoice templates provide a column for entering a quantity or unit price, but you can type that information in a description column if needed.
2. Personalize the template by adding your name as the company name and your school's address, city, state, ZIP Code, and phone as the company information. Fill in other company or invoice information with fictitious information if necessary.
3. Using today's date, create invoice 136 to:

   Leslie Taylor
   HBC Enterprises
   1240 7th Street West
   St. Paul, MN 55102
   888-555-6954
   taylor@emcp.net

   a. Type the body of the invoice using the following information:

Qty	Description	Unit Price	Total
5 hours	Social media consulting	65.00	325.00

   b. Add or delete other information as needed so the invoice is of mailable quality and does not have any placeholders with missing information.
4. Save the document in the Ch6 folder within the Assessments folder on your storage medium as **InvoiceTemplate-YourName**.
5. Submit the assessment to your instructor in the manner she or he has requested.
6. Close the document.

Assessment 6.5 Visual—Campus Flyer from Template

Type: Individual

Deliverable: Campus Flyer

1. Create a flyer for your school campus similar to the one shown in the Assessment 6.5 Campus Flyer below. Use a current date and a location suitable for concerts on or near your campus. Add current popular band names to the *FEATURING* section. Enter a fictitious web address and sponsor information. Make any other changes you think are necessary.

Note: Search for the template shown using the keywords student flyer *at the New backstage area.*

2. Save the flyer in the Ch6 folder within the Assessments folder on your storage medium as **CampusBandBattleFlyer-YourName**.

3. Submit the assessment to your instructor in the manner she or he has requested.

4. Close the document.

View

Model Answer

Compare your completed file with the model answer.

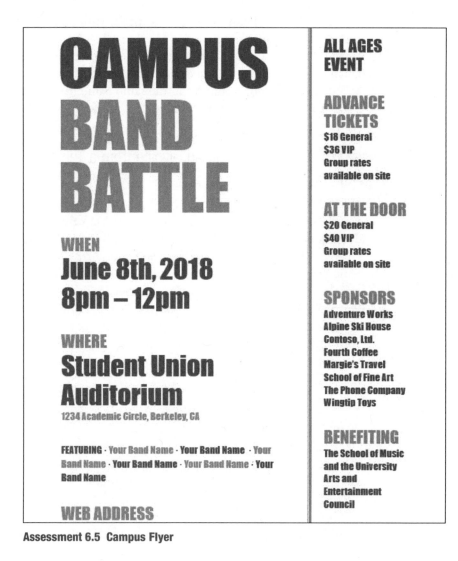

Assessment 6.5 Campus Flyer

◆▶**Audio File**   **Assessment 6.6** 🎧 Audio—Internet Research and Composing a New Document

Type: Individual or Pairs
Deliverable: Word document

You are asked to help with a project on social media by creating a document that describes what you read online after researching two to three recent events where social media was used to promote social good. The project manager has left you a voicemail with information about the project.

1. Listen to the audio file **SocialMediaForSocialGood_instructions**.
2. Complete the research and compose the document as instructed.
3. Save the document in the Ch6 folder within the Assessments folder on your storage medium as **SocialMediaResearch-YourName**.
4. Submit the assessment to your instructor in the manner she or he has requested.
5. Close the document.

Assessment 6.7 🅽 Sending Assessment Work to OneNote Notebook

Type: Individual
Deliverable: New Page in Shared OneNote notebook

1. Start OneNote and open the MyAssessments notebook created in Chapter 4, Assessment 4.4.
2. Make Word the active section and then add a new page titled *Chapter 6 Assessments*.
3. Switch to Word. For each assessment that you completed, open the document, send the assessment to OneNote 2016 selecting the Chapter 6 Assessments page in the Word section in the MyAssessments notebook, and then close the document.
4. Close your MyAssessments notebook in OneNote and then close OneNote.
5. Close Word.
6. Submit the assessment to your instructor in the manner she or he has requested.

Study Tools

**Study Tools**

Study tools, including a slide presentation and Quick Steps, are available from this ebook page.

Review Exercises

**Review Exercises**

Multiple Choice, Matching, and Completion exercises give you an opportunity to review and reinforce your understanding of the material covered in this chapter.

**SNAP**

If you are a SNAP user, go to your SNAP Assignments page to complete the review exercises.

SNAP Exercises

**SNAP**

If you are a SNAP user, go to your SNAP Assignments page to complete additional exercises available for you.

Assessments

The following assessments offer opportunities to apply what you have learned in relevant, real-world situations. Save your solution files and URLs, and submit them for evaluation as directed by your instructor.

Data Files

Assessment 7.1 Enhancing a Document with Visual Elements

Type: Individual
Deliverable: National Park Trip Planner document (continued in Assessment 7.2)

1. Open **GrandCanyonPlanner**.
2. Save the document as **GrandCanyonPlanner-YourName** in a new folder *Ch7* within the Assessments folder on your storage medium.
3. Insert, label, and edit pictures as follows:
   a. Insert the picture named ***ScorpionRidge*** at the right margin aligned with the first line of text in the first paragraph and with the *Square* text wrapping option. You determine an appropriate size for the picture with the paragraph.
   b. Insert the picture named ***BrightAngelPoint*** at the left margin aligned with the first line of text in the last paragraph and with the *Square* text wrapping option. Do not resize the picture.
   c. Add a caption below the picture inserted at Step 3a with the label text *Scorpion Ridge, North Rim*. Accept all default caption options.
   d. Add a caption below the picture inserted at Step 3b with the label text *Bright Angel Point, North Rim*. Accept all default caption options.
   e. Apply a Picture Style of your choosing to both pictures.
   f. Apply Color Saturation at 200% to both pictures.
4. Add borders, shading, and a text box as follows:
   a. Select the third sentence in the second paragraph below the subtitle *Park Entrance Fees* (begins *Admission to the park . . .*), center the text, and add an outside border.
   b. Add *Blue, Accent 1, Lighter 80%* shading to the same sentence selected in Step 4a.

c. Add a *Blue, Accent 1, 1 ½ point*, Shadow page border to the document.

d. Insert an *Austin Quote* text box and then type the following text inside the box: Grand Canyon National Park is a World Heritage Site.

e. Move the text box inserted at Step 4d so that the bottom of the text box aligns at the center of the page and bottom margin.

5. Save the revised document using the same name (**GrandCanyonPlanner–YourName**).

6. Leave the document open if you are continuing to Assessment 7.2; otherwise, close the document and submit the assessment to your instructor in the manner she or he has requested.

Assessment 7.2 Inserting, Formatting, and Modifying a Table into a Document

Type: Individual

Deliverable: National Park Trip Planner document

Note: You must have completed Assessment 7.1 before starting this assessment.

1. If necessary, open **GrandCanyonPlanner–YourName**.

2. Position the insertion point at the end of the document text and press Enter until you create a new blank line at the left margin below the picture of Bright Angel Point.

3. Insert a 5 x 5 table and then type the following text in the table grid at the default table cell options:

Rim	Trail Name	Round Trip Distance	Round Trip Estimated Time	Elevation Change
South	Rim Trail	13 miles (21 km)	All day depending on desired distance	200 feet (60 m)
South	Bright Angel Trail	3 miles (4.8 km) to 9.2 miles (14.8 km)	From 2 to 9 hours depending on desired distance	2,112 feet (644 m) to 3,060 feet (933 m)
North	Bright Angel Point	0.5 miles (0.8 km)	30 minutes	200 feet (60 m)
North	Widforss Trail	10 miles (16 km)	6 hours	200 feet (60 m)

4. Format the table as follows:

a. Apply a table style of your choosing.

b. Deselect the *First Column* table style option if it is selected.

c. Change the font size to 10 for all of the text in the table cells.

5. Modify the layout of the table as follows:

a. Set the width of the first column to 0.6 inches, and the third, fourth, and fifth columns to 1.5 inches.

b. Align all table cells at the center horizontally and vertically.

c. Insert a new row above row 4 and then type the following text in the new table cells:

South	Kaibab Trail	1.8 miles (2.9 km) to 6 miles (9.7 km)	From 1 to 6 hours depending on desired distance	600 feet (180 m) to 2,040 feet (622 m)

d. Insert a new row at the bottom of the table and then type the following text in the table cells:

North	Kaibab Trail	1.4 miles (2.3 km) to 4 miles (6.4 km)	From 1 to 4 hours depending on desired distance	800 feet (245 m) to 1,450 feet (445 m)

6. If necessary, delete extra space above or below the table to make sure the text box remains at the bottom center of the page.

7. Save the revised document using the same name (**GrandCanyonPlanner-YourName**).
8. Submit the assessment to your instructor in the manner she or he has requested.
9. Close the document.

◆ **Data Files**   **Assessment 7.3** Completing a Research Report with Formatting, Citations, and Works Cited

Type: Individual
Deliverable: Academic Paper in MLA Format

1. Open **EtanerceptEssay**.
2. Use Save As to change the file name to **EtanerceptEssay-YourName**, saving in the Ch7 folder within Assessments.
3. Select the entire document and change the font, line and paragraph spacing, and paragraph indents to conform to MLA guidelines (see Table 7.1 in Topic 7.6). **Hint:** *Turn on the display of nonprinting symbols to determine where paragraphs end to correctly complete the first line indent formatting.*
4. Insert your name, your instructor's name, the title of your course, and the current date at the top of the first page as per MLA guidelines (see Table 7.1 in Topic 7.6).
5. Add page numbering one space after your last name at the right margin in a header and format the header text to the same font and font size as the rest of the document.
6. Edit existing citations in the document as follows:
   a. Edit the source for Bradley and Desmeules in the first paragraph to change the second author's first name from *Marie* to *Mary*, and the page from *215* to *225*.
   b. Change the page from *61* to *65* for the Hashkes and Laxer citation at the end of the indented quotation on page 2.
7. Position the insertion point at the end of the quotation that reads "*The Etanercept injection is used to reduce signs and symptoms of active arthritis . . . This medicine may also slow the progression of damage to the body from active arthritis or rheumatoid arthritis*" and insert a new citation referencing *par. 14* from the following new source:

Type of Source	Document From Web site		
Author	Jarvis, B.; Faulds, D.		
Name of Web Page	Etanercept: a review of its use in rheumatoid arthritis		
Name of Web Site	PubMed, US National Library of Medicine		
Year	1999	*Month Accessed*	March
Month	June	*Day Accessed*	15
Year Accessed	2018	*Medium*	Web

8. Position the insertion point at the end of the quotation that reads "*When Etanercept is administered alone or in combination with methotrexate in patients with refractory rheumatoid arthritis, significant reductions in disease activity occur within two weeks and are sustained for at least 6 months*" and cite *par. 20* from the Jarvis and Faulds source.
9. Position the insertion point at the end of the sentence that reads *Missed doses will mean that the TNF protein is no longer being effectively controlled and inflammation, pain, and disease progression will quickly return within a month after stopping treatment* and insert a new citation referencing *par. 12* from the following new source:

Type of Source	Document From Web site		
Author	(leave blank)		
Name of Web Page	Medication Guide: Enbrel (Etanercept)		
Name of Web Site	Immunex Corporation		
Year	2011	*Month Accessed*	March
Month	December	*Day Accessed*	25
Year Accessed	2018	*Medium*	Web

10. Create and format a Works Cited page on a separate page at the end of the document.
11. Save the revised document using the same name (**EtanerceptEssay–YourName**).
12. Submit the assessment to your instructor in the manner she or he has requested and then close the document.

Assessment 7.4 Resume and Cover Letter with Comments

Type: Individual
Deliverable: Personal Resume and Cover Letter Targeted to a Specific Job Ad

1. Find a recent job ad for a position in your field of study.
2. Choose a resume template that you like and create a new resume for yourself that could be used as an application for the job ad.
3. Insert at least two comments in the resume. Each comment should be associated with an entry in your resume and pose a specific question to your instructor asking him or her for tips on how to improve the entry, or provide additional explanation as to the writing style or tone that you used.
4. Choose a cover letter template that you like and write a cover letter to enclose with the resume written specifically for the requirements in the job ad.
5. Add the URL or other source for the job ad that you used for this assessment in a comment associated with the current date text in the cover letter.
6. Save the resume as **Resume–YourName** and save the cover letter as **CoverLetter–YourName**.
7. Submit the resume and cover letter to your instructor in the manner she or he has requested.

◆ Data Files Assessment 7.5 Enhance and Format a Tourist Information Document

Type: Individual
Deliverable: Travel Information Flyer

1. Open **HangzhouInfo**.
2. Format the document as shown in the Assessment 7.5 Hangzhou Informational Flyer on the next page, using the following information to help with some of the formats:
   a. The font is 11-point Book Antiqua for the body of the document and 16-point Book Antiqua for the title and subtitle.
   b. The subheadings have the Subtitle style applied and then formatted to 14-point *Dark Blue* font color.
   c. Substitute your name in the footer in place of *Student Name*.
   d. The picture at the right margin is named ***Hangzhou*** with the *Simple Frame, Black* picture style; locate the image shown at the left margin from the web by searching using the keyword *pagoda* (or use the student data file ***pagoda***); the text box is the *Grid Quote* with the font formatting changed to 12-point Book Antiqua and the case changed.
   e. Use your best judgment to match other formatting shown and not specified in Step 2.
3. Save the revised document as **HangzhouInfo–YourName** in the Ch7 folder within Assessments.
4. Submit the assessment to your instructor in the manner she or he has requested.
5. Close the document.

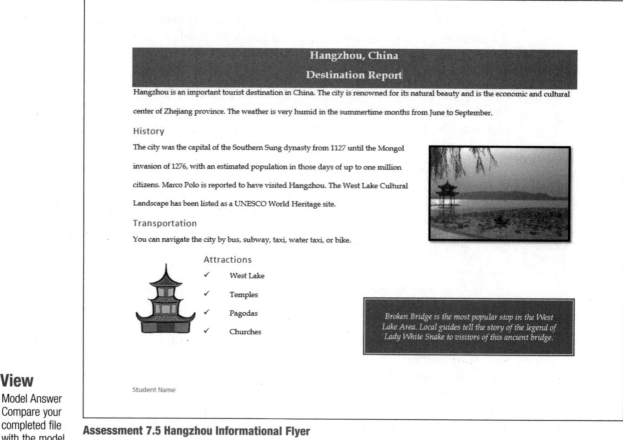

Assessment 7.5 Hangzhou Informational Flyer

Audio File   Assessment 7.6   Composing a New Flyer

Type: Individual or Pairs
Deliverable: Food Drive Flyer

Create a flyer for the school's food drive campaign in support of the local food bank to be conducted on the fifteenth and sixteenth of next month. The organizer has left you a voice mail with details about the information to be included in the flyer.

1. Listen to the audio file **FoodDriveFlyer_instructions.** The file is located in the Ch7 folder in the Student_Data_Files folder on your storage medium.
2. Create the flyer including the details requested by the organizer in the voice mail message.
3. Save the flyer in the Ch7 folder within the Assessments folder on your storage medium as **FoodDriveFlyer-YourName**.
4. Submit the assessment to your instructor in the manner she or he has requested.
5. Close the document.

Assessment 7.7 N Sending Assessment Work to OneNote Notebook

Type: Individual

Deliverable: New Page in Shared OneNote notebook

1. Start OneNote and open the MyAssessments notebook created in Chapter 4, Assessment 4.4.
2. Make Word the active section and then add a new page titled *Chapter 7 Assessments*.
3. Switch to Word. For each assessment that you completed, open the document, send the assessment to OneNote 2016 selecting the Chapter 7 Assessments page in the Word section in the MyAssessments notebook, and then close the document.
4. Close your MyAssessments notebook in OneNote and then close OneNote.
5. Close Word.
6. Submit the assessment to your instructor in the manner she or he has requested.

Study Tools

 **Study Tools**

Study tools, including a slide presentation and Quick Steps, are available from this ebook page.

Review Exercises

 Review Exercises

Multiple Choice, Matching, and Completion exercises give you an opportunity to review and reinforce your understanding of the material covered in this chapter.

SNAP

If you are a SNAP user, go to your SNAP Assignments page to complete the review exercises.

SNAP Exercises

SNAP

If you are a SNAP user, go to your SNAP Assignments page to complete additional exercises available for you.

Assessments

The following assessments offer opportunities to apply what you have learned in relevant, real–world situations. Save your solution files and URLs and submit them for evaluation as directed by your instructor.

Assessment 8.1   Creating and Editing a New Workbook

Type: Individual
Deliverable: Excel worksheet with Auction Fee Calculations (continued in Assessment 8.2)

1. Start a new blank workbook and enter the text and values in the worksheet as shown below in the Assessment 8.1 worksheet.
2. Save the workbook as **AuctionFees–YourName** in a new folder named *Ch8* within the Assessments folder on your storage medium.

	A	B	C	D	E	F	G	H	I	J
1	Fees Paid for Video Game Online Auctions									
2	Auctions ended in January									
3										
4	AuctionID	Game			Platform	Sale Price	Fee	Shipping	Fee	Total Fee
5	25687	Fallout 4			Xbox One	67.55		4.99		
6	31452	Halo 5: Guardians			Xbox One	69.5		4.99		
7	98563	Mortal Kombat X			Xbox 360	55.99		4.99		
8	17586	Call of Duty Black Ops III			Xbox 360	70		4.99		
9	32586	Batman Arkham Knight			PS 4	65.99		4.99		
10	45862	Star Wars Battlefront			PS 4	69.99		4.99		
11	13485	Fallout 4			PS 4	69.9		4.99		
12	65985	Mortal Kombat X			PS 3	52.5		4.99		
13	74586	Call of Duty Black Ops III			PS 3	53		4.99		
14	56842	Dragonball Xenoverse			PC	45.99		5		
15	43668	Grand Theft Auto V			PC	62.99		5		

 **View**
Larger Image

Assessment 8.1 worksheet

3. Enter each of the following formulas using the typing or pointing method:

   G5   =F5*.10   J5   =G5+I5
   I5   =H5*.10

4. Use the fill handle to copy each formula to the remaining rows in columns G, I, and J.
5. Type Total Fees Paid for January Auctions in B16.
6. Use the AutoSum button to calculate the totals in G16 and I16.

Note: Flash Fill may automatically calculate the total in J16; but, if no total appears in J16, calculate the total yourself.

7. Edit the worksheet as follows:
   a. Change the sale price of Halo 5: Guardians from *69.50* to *62.99*.
   b. Edit the game title for Dragonball Xenoverse to *Dragon Ball XV*.
   c. Change the shipping for Grand Theft Auto V from *5.00* to *6.50*.
   d. Type the current year one space after January in A2 so that the entry reads *Auctions ended in January 2018*. (Your year will vary.)
8. Proofread carefully to make sure the worksheet is error-free.
9. Change the scaling option to fit all columns on one page.
10. Save the revised workbook using the same name (**AuctionFees-YourName**).
11. Leave the workbook open if you are continuing to Assessment 8.2; otherwise, close the workbook and submit the assessment to your instructor in the manner she or he has requested.

Assessment 8.2 Editing and Formatting a Worksheet

Type: Individual
Deliverable: Excel worksheet with Auction Fee Calculations

Note: You must have completed Assessment 8.1 before starting this assessment.

1. If necessary, open **AuctionFees-YourName**.
2. Use Save As to change the file name to **AuctionFeesFormatted-YourName**, saving it in the same folder.
3. Insert a new row above row 7 and type the following auction item information in the appropriate cells:

   21549   Halo: The Master Chief Collection   Xbox One   59.99 (sale price)
   4.99 (shipping)

Note: The formulas in fees cells should be automatically created; however, if no fees are calculated, enter the required formulas yourself.

4. Insert a blank column between columns I and J so that the *Total Fee* column is set apart from the rest of the data.
5. Change the width of column B to *35* and then delete columns C and D.
6. Change the height of row 4 to *25* and middle-align the column headings.
7. Format the worksheet as follows:
   a. Merge and center the titles in row 1 and row 2 over columns A through I.
   b. Left-align A5:A16 and center-align E4 and G4.
   c. Apply Comma Style to D5:I17.
   d. Add a thick bottom border to A4:I4 and a top and double bottom border to E17, G17, and I17.
   e. Select A1:A2 and then change the font to Cambria, the font size to 16, and the font color to Dark Blue, and apply bold formatting.
   f. Select A4:I4, apply bold formatting, and add Gold, Accent 4 shading.
   g. Apply bold formatting to B17, E17, G17, and I17.
8. Select A5:I16 and open the Sort dialog box. Sort the range first by the *Game* column in ascending order. Add another sort level and then sort by the platform in ascending order.
9. Change the worksheet to landscape orientation.

10. Save the revised workbook using the same name (**AuctionFeesFormatted-YourName**).
11. Turn on the display of cell formulas.
12. Change the scaling option to print the entire worksheet on one page.
13. Use Save As to save a copy of the worksheet with the formulas displayed as **AuctionFeesFormulas-YourName**.
14. Submit the assessment to your instructor in the manner she or he has requested.
15. Close the workbook.

◆ **Data Files**   **Assessment 8.3** Formatting with Styles and Inserting a New Worksheet

Type: Individual
Deliverable: Excel workbook with Cancer Patient Statistics in two worksheets

1. Open **CancerStatsReport**.
2. Use Save As to change the file name to **CancerStatsReport-YourName**, saving it in the Ch8 folder in Assessments.
3. Merge and center the titles in row 1 and row 2 over columns A through G.
4. Wrap the text in A3:G3.
5. Change the column widths as follows:
     Column B to *10*   Column C to *9*   Column E to *10*   Column F to *20*
6. Apply cell styles of your choosing to A1, A2, and A3:G3 to improve the appearance of the worksheet.
7. Insert a new worksheet in the workbook and change the name to *Quarter 2*.
8. Rename the ReportData worksheet *Quarter 1*.
9. Copy A1:G3 from the Quarter 1 sheet and paste it to A1 in the Quarter 2 sheet, keeping the source column widths. Edit the title in A2 so that the title references Quarter 2 instead of Quarter 1.
10. Copy A4:G30 from the Quarter 1 sheet and paste it to A4 in the Quarter 2 sheet.
11. In the Quarter 2 sheet, clear the contents of A4:A30 and G4:G30.
12. Set the print settings for each worksheet to *Fit All Columns on One Page*.
13. Freeze the first three rows in each worksheet.
14. Save the revised workbook using the same name (**CancerStatsReport-YourName**).
15. Submit the assessment to your instructor in the manner she or he has requested.
16. Close the workbook.

Assessment 8.4 Creating a Weekly Schedule from a Template

Type: Individual
Deliverable: Worksheet with a schedule for the current week

1. You learned about creating new documents from templates in Word in Chapter 6. Excel also has many templates available for creating new workbooks that are grouped into categories and located using the search text box at the New backstage area. Search for and select a template of your choosing to create a weekly schedule. Use the search phrase *time schedule* to find a suitable template.
2. Enter your schedule for the current week into the new worksheet. Make sure the schedule is complete with all of your classes and other activities.
3. Save the workbook in the Ch8 folder within Assessments as **WeeklySchedule-YourName**.
4. Submit the assessment to your instructor in the manner she or he has requested.
5. Close the workbook.

Assessment 8.5 👁 Visual—Creating a Party Expense Worksheet

Type: Individual
Deliverable: Anniversary Party Expense Worksheet

1. Create a worksheet similar to the Assessment 8.5 worksheet below, with the following information:
   a. The amounts in the *Difference* column are formulas that calculate the actual expenses minus the estimated expenses, and the values shown in row 12 are formulas.
   b. The width of column A is 42, and the width of columns B, C, and D is 12. The height of row 1 is 36 and the height of row 2 is 24.
   c. A2:D2 has the Accent6 cell style applied.
   d. The font used in A1 is 18-point Cambria. The font for the rest of the cells in the worksheet is Book Antiqua at the default size.
   e. Use your best judgment for any other format options such as alignment and shading.
2. Save the worksheet in the Ch8 folder within the Assessments folder as **PartyExpenses-YourName**.
3. Submit the assessment to your instructor in the manner she or he has requested.
4. Close the workbook.

View

Model Answer

Compare your completed file with the model answer.

	A	B	C	D
1	**Mom and Dad's Anniversary Party Budget**			
2	Item	Estimated	Actual	Difference
3	Decorations	$ 325.00	$ 342.00	$ 17.00
4	Flowers	625.00	601.00	- 24.00
5	Entertainer	550.00	550.00	-
6	Photographer and prints	875.00	1,125.00	250.00
7	Rental of reception room	150.00	150.00	-
8	Rental of tables, chairs, plates, and cutlery	190.00	175.00	- 15.00
9	Food and drinks	2,245.00	2,100.00	- 145.00
10	Invitations	75.00	81.00	6.00
11	Miscellaneous supplies	100.00	112.00	12.00
12	**Total Expenses**	$ 5,135.00	$ 5,236.00	$ 101.00

Assessment 8.5 worksheet

Audio File   Assessment 8.6 🎧 Audio—Internet Research and Composing a New Workbook

Type: Individual or Pairs
Deliverable: Excel workbook with costs for a spring break trip

You are asked to help the president of the student union at your school create a workbook with costs for five popular spring break destinations for a prize that includes a free trip with spending money. The student union office assistant has left you a phone message explaining what to include in the workbook.

1. Listen to the audio file named ***SpringBreakContest_instructions***.
2. Complete the research and compose the worksheet as instructed.
3. Save the workbook in the Ch8 folder within Assessments as **SpringBreakContest-YourName**.
4. Submit the assessment to your instructor in the manner she or he has requested.
5. Close the workbook.

Assessment 8.7 [N] OneNote—Sending Completed Assessments to Your Notebook

Type: Individual

Deliverable: New Page in OneNote notebook

1. Start OneNote and open the MyAssessments notebook you created in Chapter 4, Assessment 4.4.
2. Make Excel the active section and add a new page titled *Chapter 8 Assessments*.
3. Switch to Excel. For each Chapter 8 assessment that you complete, open the file, send the assessment to OneNote 2016 (selecting the Chapter 8 Assessments page in the Excel section in the MyAssessments notebook), and then close the workbook. Make sure to include all worksheets in workbooks with more than one sheet tab.
4. Close your MyAssessments notebook in OneNote and close OneNote.
5. Close Excel.
6. Submit the assessment to your instructor in the manner she or he has requested.

Study Tools

Study tools, including a slide presentation and Quick Steps, are available from this ebook page.

Review Exercises

Multiple Choice, Matching, and Completion exercises give you an opportunity to review and reinforce your understanding of the material covered in this chapter.

SNAP If you are a SNAP user, go to your SNAP Assignments page to complete the review exercises.

SNAP Exercises

SNAP If you are a SNAP user, go to your SNAP Assignments page to complete additional exercises available for you.

Assessments

The following assessments offer opportunities to apply what you have learned in relevant, real-world situations. Save your solution files and URLs, and submit them for evaluation as directed by your instructor.

Data Files **Assessment 9.1** Adding Statistical, Date, Financial, and Logical Functions to a Workbook

Type: Individual
Deliverable: Worksheet with Auction Fee Financial Analysis and Mortgage Options

1. Open **AuctionFeesandMortgagePlanner**.
2. Use Save As to change the file name to **AuctionFeesandMortgagePlanner-YourName** in a new folder named *Ch9* within the Assessments folder on your storage medium.
3. In J2 enter a formula that will insert the current date and update the date each time the workbook is opened or printed.
4. Assign the following names to the cells indicated:
   C2 AuctionFee   G2 PaymentFee
5. Complete the formulas required in the worksheet using the following information:
   a. In column B, calculate the payment due dates as 5 days following the auction end date.
   b. In column D, calculate the auction fees as the sale price times the auction fee percentage. Use the range name created in Step 4 in the formula.
   c. In column E, calculate the payment processing fees as the sale price times the payment fee percentage. Use the range name created in Step 4 in the formula.
   d. In column F, calculate the net auction earnings as the sale price minus the auction fee and payment processing fee.
   e. In column G, calculate the amount to transfer to the checking account as the value that resides in net auction earnings for those instances in which

the net auction earnings are less than or equal to $20.00; otherwise, calculate the amount as 50 percent of the net auction earnings.

f. In column H, calculate the amount to transfer to the investment account as 50 percent of the net auction earnings for those instances in which the net auction earnings are more than $20.00; otherwise, show zero in the cell.

g. In column J, calculate the three sets of required statistics. Use the labels to help you determine the functions and arguments required.

h. In row 27, calculate totals for columns C through H.

6. Format C2 and G2 to Percent Style, format the dates in columns A and B to the style *14-Mar*, and format all other values to Comma Style.

7. Make MortgageAnalysis the active worksheet and complete the formulas required in the worksheet using the following information:

a. In B7 and D7, calculate the estimated monthly payments.

b. In B9 and D9, calculate the total paid over the life of each mortgage.

8. For each worksheet, change page layout options as necessary to make sure the worksheet will fit on one page centered horizontally and with your name centered in a header, the file name at the left margin in a footer, and the sheet name at the right margin in a footer.

9. Save the revised workbook using the same name (**AuctionFeesandMortgagePlanner-YourName**).

10. Close the workbook.

11. Submit the assessment to your instructor in the manner she or he has requested.

◆ **Data Files   Assessment 9.2** Creating and Modifying Charts

Type: Individual

Deliverable: Worksheet with Charts Illustrating Vacation Destination Statistics

1. Open **VacDestinations**.

2. Use Save As to change the file name to **VacDestinations-YourName**, saving in the Ch9 folder within Assessments.

3. With the TopVacDestinations sheet active, create a pie chart at the bottom left of the worksheet area that graphs the Worldwide destinations and percentages. Create a second pie chart at the bottom right of the worksheet area that graphs the United States and Canada destinations and percentages. Add and/or modify chart elements you think are appropriate to make sure the charts are easy to read and understand.

4. With the NationalParks worksheet active, create a clustered column chart that graphs the national parks and visitors. Position the chart where you think the chart looks good and add and/or modify chart elements you think are appropriate to make sure the chart is easy to read and understand.

5. With the InternationalTravel worksheet active, select A3:D15 and create a line chart in a chart sheet named *InternationalTravelChart*. Add and/or modify chart elements you think are appropriate to make sure the chart is easy to read and understand.

6. For the three worksheets with charts, change page layout options as necessary to make sure the worksheet will fit on one page centered vertically and with your name centered in a header, the file name at the left margin in a footer, and the sheet name at the right margin in a footer. *Hint: Add the header and footer in the InternationalTravelChart sheet using the Page Setup hyperlink in Print Preview.*

7. Save the revised workbook using the same name (**VacDestinations-YourName**).

8. Close the workbook.

9. Submit the assessment to your instructor in the manner she or he has requested.

Data Files   **Assessment 9.3** Adding Sparklines and Comments

Type: Individual

Deliverable: Worksheet with Comments and Sparklines Illustrating School Newspaper Budget Values

1. Open **SchoolPaperBudget**.
2. Use Save As to change the file name to **SchoolPaperBudget-YourName**, saving in the Ch9 folder within Assessments.
3. Create line sparkline charts in column K that graph the budget values for September through April. Show the high and low points. Add and/or modify any other sparkline elements you think are appropriate.
4. Add the following comments to the cells indicated:
   E9   Christmas ads expected to increase 10% this year.
   I5   New ISP contract takes effect in April.
   I9   Consider end-of-year special pricing to raise ad revenue.
5. Display the worksheet in Print Preview and use the <u>Page Setup</u> hyperlink to open the Page Setup dialog box. Change the *Comments* option to *At end of sheet* in the Sheet tab.
6. Save the revised workbook using the same name (**SchoolPaperBudget-YourName**).
7. Close the workbook.
8. Submit the assessment to your instructor in the manner she or he has requested.

Data Files   **Assessment 9.4** Working with Tables

Type: Individual

Deliverable: Worksheet with Model Home Pricing Table

1. Open **ModelHomes**.
2. Use Save As to change the file name to **ModelHomes-YourName**, saving in the Ch9 folder within Assessments.
3. Format A5:E20 as a table.
4. Change to a table style of your choosing.
5. Sort in ascending order by the *Description of upgrade* column.
6. Add totals below each model home that sum the total cost of the upgrades.
7. In A23 enter the text TOTAL MODEL HOME PRICE WITH ALL UPGRADES.
8. Create formulas in B23:E23 that show the total price of each model home with the base price and total upgrade costs.
9. Change the worksheet to landscape orientation, centered vertically, and with your name centered in a header and the file name centered in a footer.
10. Save the revised workbook using the same name (**ModelHomes-YourName**).
11. Close the workbook.
12. Submit the assessment to your instructor in the manner she or he has requested.

Assessment 9.5 Visual—Creating a Worksheet and Charts to Show Food Drive Results

Type: Individual

Deliverable: Worksheet with Food Drive Results and Charts

1. Create a worksheet and charts similar to the one shown in the Assessment 9.5 worksheet on the next page with the following additional information:
   a. The workbook theme is *Frame*.
   b. The charts are clustered bar charts using *Style 13*.
   c. Set the height for row 1 to *30.00* and row 2 to *21.00*. Set the width of column A to *16.50* and column B to *10.00*.

d. The font size for row 1 is 18 points and row 2 is 12 points.

e. Use your best judgment for any other format options such as shading.

2. Save the worksheet in the Ch9 folder within the Assessments folder as **FoodDrive-YourName**.

3. Change the top margin to 1.5 inches. Make sure the worksheet will fit on one page in portrait orientation with your name centered in a header and the file name centered in a footer.

4. Save the workbook again using the same name (**FoodDrive-YourName**).

5. Close the workbook.

6. Submit the assessment to your instructor in the manner she or he has requested.

◆▷ View

Model Answer

Compare your completed file with the model answer.

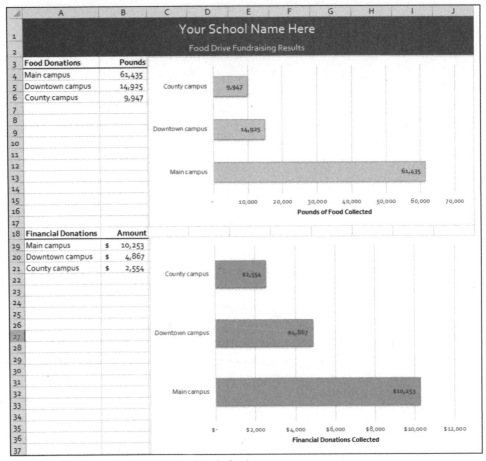

Assessment 9.5 Food Drive worksheet and charts

◆▷ Audio File   Assessment 9.6 🎧 Audio—Internet Research and Composing a New Workbook

Type: Individual or Pairs

Deliverable: Worksheet with Membership Statistical Data and Line Chart

The academic manager of the business school has asked for your help preparing a worksheet and line chart with membership statistics from the launch of the Instagram social media website in October 2010 to today. The school assistant has left you a voice mail with instructions.

1. Listen to the audio file **InstagramUserData_instructions**.
2. Complete the research and compose the worksheet and chart as instructed.
3. Save the workbook in the Ch9 folder within Assessments as **InstagramUserData-YourName**.
4. Close the workbook.
5. Submit the assessment to your instructor in the manner she or he has requested.

Assessment 9.7 N OneNote—Sending Assessment Work to OneNote Notebook

Type: Individual
Deliverable: New Page in Shared OneNote notebook

1. Start OneNote and open the MyAssessments notebook created in Chapter 4, Assessment 4.4.
2. Make Excel the active section and add a new page titled *Chapter 9 Assessments*.
3. Switch to Excel. For each assessment that you complete, open the workbook, send the assessment to OneNote 2016 selecting the Chapter 9 Assessments page in the Excel section in the MyAssessments notebook, then close the workbook. Make sure to include all worksheets in workbooks with more than one sheet tab.
4. Close your MyAssessments notebook in OneNote and then close OneNote.
5. Close Excel.
6. Submit the assessment to your instructor in the manner she or he has requested.

Study Tools

Study tools, including a slide presentation and Quick Steps, are available from this ebook page.

Review Exercises

Multiple Choice, Matching, and Completion exercises give you an opportunity to review and reinforce your understanding of the material covered in this chapter.

If you are a SNAP user, go to your SNAP Assignments page to complete the review exercises.

SNAP Exercises

If you are a SNAP user, go to your SNAP Assignments page to complete additional exercises available for you.

Assessments

The following assessments offer opportunities to apply what you have learned in relevant, real–world situations. Save your solution files and URLs, and submit them for evaluation as directed by your instructor.

Assessment 10.1 Creating and Editing a New Presentation

Type: Individual
Deliverable: Presentation about world and US landmarks (continued in Assessments 10.2 and 10.3)

1. Start a new presentation, choosing a theme and variant that you like.
2. Save the presentation as **Landmarks–YourName** in a new folder named *Ch10* within the Assessments folder on your storage medium.
3. Create slides including multilevel lists, a table, and a comparison slide with the following information:

Slide 1	Title	Famous Landmarks
	Subtitle	Your Name
Slide 2	Title	World and National Landmarks
	List	Top 5 World Landmarks
		Top 5 US Landmarks
		Survey Results
		Honorable Mentions
Slide 3	Title	Top 5 World Landmarks
	Multilevel List	The Pyramid of Khufu
		Located in Giza, Egypt
		Largest pyramid ever built
		The Great Wall of China
		Completed during the Ming dynasty (1368 to 1644)

Acropolis
    UNESCO World Heritage Site
    Parthenon Greek temple
Eiffel Tower
    18,000 metallic parts joined by 2,500,000 rivets
Taj Mahal
    Agra, India

Slide 4	Title	Top 5 US Landmarks
	List	Statue of Liberty, New York
		Grand Canyon, Arizona
		Mount Rushmore, South Dakota
		Independence Hall, Philadelphia
		The National Mall, District of Columbia

Slide 5   Title   Survey Results

	Table	Social Media Website	Votes Cast
		Facebook	345,985
		Instagram	295,672
		Twitter	420,870
		Tumblr	155,329

Slide 6   Title   Honorable Mentions

	Comparison	World Landmarks	US Landmarks
	Slide Layout	Stonehenge, UK	Freedom Trail, Boston
		Edinburgh Castle, Scotland	Fort Sumter, Charleston
		Buckingham Palace, UK	The Alamo, San Antonio
		Machu Picchu, Peru	Gateway Arch, St. Louis

4. Perform a spelling check and carefully proofread each slide, making corrections as needed.
5. Edit Slide 3 as follows:
   a. Delete the entry *Largest pyramid ever built.*
   b. Delete the entry *UNESCO World Heritage Site.*
   c. Insert the text *Tower located in Paris has* before the entry that begins *18,000 metallic parts.*
   d. Insert the text *Marble mausoleum located in* before *Agra, India.*
6. Edit Slide 5, changing the votes cast by Facebook from *345,985* to *543,589.*
7. Save the revised presentation using the same name (**Landmarks-YourName**).
8. Leave the presentation open if you are continuing to Assessment 10.2; otherwise close the presentation and submit the assessment to your instructor in the manner she or he has requested.

Assessment 10.2 Editing and Formatting a Presentation

Type: Individual

Deliverable: Presentation about world and US landmarks (continued in Assessment 10.3)

Note: You must have completed Assessment 10.1 before starting this assessment.

1. If necessary, open **Landmarks-YourName**.
2. Change the theme and variant to another design of your choosing. Check each slide after you change the theme for corrections that may be needed. For example, a theme that uses the All Caps font in a title or subtitle may cause changes in capitalization when the theme is changed to one that does not use the All Caps font.

3. Display the slide master and make the following changes to the top slide in the hierarchy:
   a. Change the font color for all the titles to another font color of your choosing.
   b. Change the bullet character to a different symbol and color than the one used in the theme.
4. Display Slide 5 and modify the table layout and design as follows:
   a. Change the width of the first column to 3.5 inches.
   b. Change the width of the second column to 1.75 inches.
   c. Center-align the entries in the second column.
   d. Change the table style to another style of your choosing.
   e. Move the table so that the table is approximately centered below the title text.
5. Display Slide 6 and make the following changes:
   a. Change the bullet character to a different symbol than the symbol that was used on the slide master for each of the two lists.
   b. Resize the left list placeholder so that the right border ends just after the longest entry in the list. Resize the left title placeholder to the same width as the list.
   c. Move the left title and list placeholders closer to the right title and list. Align the two titles and lists so that they are approximately centered below the title text.
6. Save the revised presentation using the same name (**Landmarks–YourName**).
7. Leave the presentation open if you are continuing to Assessment 10.3; otherwise, close the presentation and submit the assessment to your instructor in the manner she or he has requested.

Assessment 10.3 Rearranging Slides and Adding Notes and Comments

Type: Individual
Deliverable: Presentation about world and US landmarks

Note: You must have completed Assessments 10.1 and 10.2 before starting this assessment.

1. If necessary, open **Landmarks–YourName**.
2. Move the *Survey Results* slide so that it becomes the third slide in the presentation.
3. Move the *Honorable Mentions* slide after the *Survey Results* slide.
4. Display Slide 2 and edit the bulleted list to reposition the bottom two bulleted list items so they become the top two bulleted list items.
5. Display the *Survey Results* slide and then type the following text in the notes pane:
   Our first survey using social media for reader voting was a phenomenal success. Plans for next year's survey are to expand voting to include other social media sites. Ask the audience for suggestions.
6. Display the *Honorable Mentions* slide and then type the following text in the notes pane:
   All honorable mentions had at least 20,000 votes.
7. Display the *Top 5 World Landmarks* slide, select the bulleted list text below *Eiffel Tower*, and then type the following comment:
   Should I remove the number of parts and rivets?
8. Display the *Top 5 US Landmarks* slide and then type the following comment for the entire slide:
   Should I add the number of votes for each landmark?
9. Save the revised presentation using the same name (**Landmarks–YourName**).
10. Submit the assessment to your instructor in the manner she or he has requested and then close the presentation.

Assessment 10.4 Internet Research and Creating a Presentation from a Template

Type: Individual or Pairs

Deliverable: Presentation about inventions

1. Start a new presentation, browsing the *Education* category of templates and choosing a template that you like.
2. Create slides for a presentation about the inventions listed below. For each invention, research four to five interesting facts about the invention and add the information in a bulleted list on the slide.

Slide 1   (You determine an appropriate title and subtitle.)
Slide 2   (You determine an appropriate introductory slide for the presentation.)
Slide 3   The Telephone
Slide 4   The Television
Slide 5   The Automobile
Slide 6   The Light bulb

3. Delete slides that were downloaded as part of the template that are not needed for this presentation.
4. Save the presentation in the Ch10 folder within the Assessments folder as **Inventions-YourName**.
5. Submit the assessment to your instructor in the manner she or he has requested.
6. Close the presentation.

Assessment 10.5 👁 Visual—Creating a Graduation Party Planning Presentation

Type: Individual

Deliverable: Presentation on college graduation party planning

1. Create a presentation similar to the one shown in the Assessment 10.5 Graduation Party Planning Presentation on the next page with the following additional information:
   a. The theme is *Integral* with one of the variants selected.
   b. The bullet symbols have been changed on the slide master.
   c. The font color for the slide titles has been changed on the slide master. Use your best judgment to choose a similar color.
   d. Use your best judgment to determine other formatting, placeholder size, and alignment options.
2. Save the presentation in the Ch10 folder within the Assessments folder as **GradParty-YourName**.
3. Submit the assessment to your instructor in the manner she or he has requested.
4. Close the presentation.

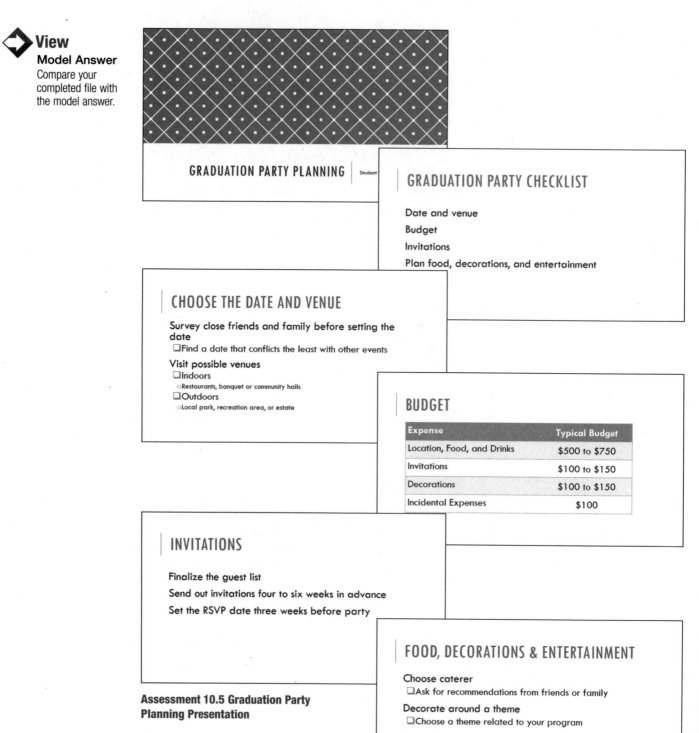

View
Model Answer
Compare your completed file with the model answer.

GRADUATION PARTY PLANNING | Student

GRADUATION PARTY CHECKLIST

Date and venue
Budget
Invitations
Plan food, decorations, and entertainment

CHOOSE THE DATE AND VENUE

Survey close friends and family before setting the date
☐ Find a date that conflicts the least with other events

Visit possible venues
☐ Indoors
  ○ Restaurants, banquet or community halls
☐ Outdoors
  ○ Local park, recreation area, or estate

BUDGET

Expense	Typical Budget
Location, Food, and Drinks	$500 to $750
Invitations	$100 to $150
Decorations	$100 to $150
Incidental Expenses	$100

INVITATIONS

Finalize the guest list
Send out invitations four to six weeks in advance
Set the RSVP date three weeks before party

FOOD, DECORATIONS & ENTERTAINMENT

Choose caterer
☐ Ask for recommendations from friends or family
Decorate around a theme
☐ Choose a theme related to your program
Entertainment
☐ Assemble your favorite music playlists
☐ Plan to tell a few humorous stories from school

Assessment 10.5 Graduation Party Planning Presentation

Audio File **Assessment 10.6** Audio—Internet Research and Composing a New Presentation

Type: Individual or Pairs

Deliverable: Presentation about US or Canadian historical figure

You have been asked to help the president of the school's history society with a presentation for a guest speaker at a new activity called History Conversations. Research a US or Canadian historical figure and prepare a six-slide presentation with the main facts about the person and his or her significance in US or Canadian history.

1. Listen to the audio file named ***HistoricalFigure_Instructions***.
2. Complete the research and compose the presentation as instructed.
3. Save the presentation in the Ch10 folder within the Assessments folder as **HistoricalFigure-YourName**.
4. Submit the assessment to your instructor in the manner she or he has requested.
5. Close the presentation.

Assessment 10.7 OneNote—Sending Assessment Work to OneNote Notebook

Type: Individual

Deliverable: New page in Shared OneNote notebook

1. Start OneNote and open the MyAssessments notebook created in Chapter 4, Assessment 4.4.
2. Make PowerPoint the active section and then add a new page titled *Chapter 10 Assessments*.
3. Switch to PowerPoint. For each assessment that you completed, open the presentation, send the slides formatted as handouts with six slides horizontal per page, and with your name in a header to OneNote 2016, selecting the *Chapter 10 Assessments* page in the *PowerPoint* section in the MyAssessments notebook, then close the presentation, saving changes if prompted to do so.
4. Close your MyAssessments notebook in OneNote and then close OneNote.
5. Close PowerPoint.
6. Submit the assessment to your instructor in the manner she or he has requested.

Study Tools

Study Tools   Study tools, including a slide presentation and Quick Steps, are available from this ebook page.

Review Exercises

Review Exercises   Multiple Choice, Matching, and Completion exercises give you an opportunity to review and reinforce your understanding of the material covered in this chapter.

SNAP   If you are a SNAP user, go to your SNAP Assignments page to complete the review exercises.

SNAP Exercises

SNAP   If you are a SNAP user, go to your SNAP Assignments page to complete additional exercises available for you.

Assessments

The following assessments offer opportunities to apply what you have learned in relevant, real-world situations. Save your solution files and URLs, and submit them for evaluation as directed by your instructor.

Assessment 11.1 Adding Graphics to a Presentation

Type: Individual
Deliverable: Presentation about World War I (continued in Assessments 11.2 and 11.3)

1. Open **WorldWarIPres**.
2. Use Save As to change the file name to **WorldWarIPres–YourName** in a new folder *Ch11* within the Assessments folder on your storage medium.
3. Make Slide 2 the active slide in the slide pane and then insert the picture *MilitaryGroupWWI* at the bottom right of the slide, resizing the image as needed.
4. Make Slide 6 the active slide in the slide pane and then insert the picture *WeaponWWI* at the right side of the slide next to the bulleted list, resizing the image as needed.
5. Make Slide 3 the active slide in the slide pane and then convert the bullet list to a SmartArt graphic. You determine an appropriate SmartArt layout. Apply a SmartArt Style of your choosing. Resize and/or make other formatting changes you think are appropriate.
6. Make Slide 4 the active slide in the slide pane and then convert the bullet list to the same SmartArt layout you used on Slide 3. Apply the same design and formatting changes so that Slide 3 and Slide 4 are consistent.
7. Make Slide 5 the active slide in the slide pane and then insert a chart using the following information:
   a. Choose the *Bar* category and the *Clustered Bar* chart type.
   b. Enter the following data in the chart data grid. Delete columns and rows with sample data that are not needed for the chart.
      A2 Allied Forces   B2 12.6
      A3 Central Forces   B3 8.4

    c. Delete the *Series 1* legend that appears below the chart.

    d. Edit the *Series 1* chart title that appears above the chart to read *Millions of Soldiers.*

    e. Apply a chart style of your choosing.

8. Insert a shape positioned near the top right of the chart on Slide 5 using the *Explosion 1* option in the *Stars and Banners* category with the following text inside: *Allies bear 4.2 million more injuries!* Resize the shape, allowing the shape to flow outside the chart border if necessary. Apply a shape style of your choosing.

9. Insert a text box positioned below the picture on Slide 6 with the following text inside the box: *Canadian artillery loading a field gun.* Change the font size to 14 points and italicize the text.

10. Insert a text box positioned below the chart on Slide 5 and aligned at the left edge with the following text inside the box: *Source: Military Research, UK.* Italicize the text.

11. Insert a new slide after Slide 7 with a Title Only layout and type the following text as the slide title: 100 Year Anniversary. Create a WordArt object with the following text: *2014 to 2018.* Change the font size to 72 points and format the text with WordArt styles and text effects of your choosing.

12. Save the revised presentation using the same name (**WorldWarIPres-YourName**).

13. Leave the presentation open if you are continuing to Assessment 11.2; otherwise, close the presentation and submit the assessment to your instructor in the manner she or he has requested.

◆ **Data Files**   **Assessment 11.2** Adding Sound and Video

Type: Individual

Deliverable: Presentation about World War I (continued in Assessment 11.3)

Note: You must have completed Assessment 11.1 before starting this assessment.

1. If necessary, open **WorldWarIPres-YourName**.

2. Make Slide 7 with the title *American Forces in France* the active slide in the slide pane.

3. Insert the video clip ***AmericaGoesToWar*** from the Ch11 folder in Student_Data_Files on the slide. Edit the video as follows:

    a. Change the *Start* option to *Automatically.*

    b. Trim the video to start at *0:48* and end at *2:35.*

    c. Apply a video style of your choosing to the video object.

4. Add the audio clip ***BulletsandBayonets*** from the Ch11 folder in Student_Data_Files on Slide 1 with the following audio options:

    a. Change the *Start* option to *Automatically.*

    b. Change the volume to *Low.*

    c. Set the audio to play across all slides.

    d. Hide the sound icon during a slide show.

5. Type the following photo, video, and audio credits in a table on the last slide. You determine the table style, column widths, and other format options.

Slide	Item	Credit
1	Music	United States Marine Band at George Mason University
2	Photo	City of Toronto archives via Wikimedia Commons
6	Photo	Canadian Department of National Defence via Wikimedia Commons
7	Video	America Goes Over (Part I), US Army, Signal Corps via Internet Archive

6. Save the revised presentation using the same name (**WorldWarIPres-YourName**).

7. Leave the presentation open if you are continuing to Assessment 11.3; otherwise, close the presentation and submit the assessment to your instructor in the manner she or he has requested.

Assessment 11.3 Adding Transition and Animation Effects and Setting Up a Slide Show

Type: Individual

Deliverable: Self-Running Presentation about World War I

Note: You must have completed Assessments 11.1 and 11.2 before starting this assessment.

1. If necessary, open **WorldWarIPres–Your Name**.
2. Apply a transition of your choosing to all slides.
3. With Slide 2 the active slide, display the slide master and add an animation effect of your choosing to the title placeholder and the content placeholder. For each animation, change the *Start* option to *After Previous*. Return to Normal view when finished.
4. Apply an animation effect of your choosing to the following objects with the *Start* option changed to *After Previous* for each object:
   Photo on Slide 2
   Explosion shape and text box on Slide 5
   Photo and text box on Slide 6
   WordArt on Slide 8
5. Set the time for all slides to remain on the screen during a slide show to *0:15* (15 seconds).
6. Change the times for three slides as follows: Slide 1 to *0:05*; Slide 5 to *0:08*; Slide 8 to *0:05*.
7. Change the *Show type* to *Browsed by an individual (window)* and turn on the option to Loop continuously until 'Esc' at the Set Up Show dialog box.
8. Preview the slide show.
9. Save the revised presentation using the same name (**WorldWarIPres–YourName**) and then close the presentation.
10. Submit the assessment to your instructor in the manner she or he has requested.

Assessment 11.4 Creating a Self-Running Multimedia Presentation

Type: Individual or Pairs

Deliverable: Presentation with Money-Saving Strategies for College Students

1. Create a presentation with six to eight slides with your best money-saving tips you can give to college students to help students survive on limited income while in school. Incorporate graphics, sound, and video into the presentation to make the presentation interesting and communicate your ideas.
2. Apply transition and animation effects of your choosing, setting up the slide show as a self-running presentation with appropriate times assigned for each slide.
3. Save the presentation in the Ch11 folder within the Assessments folder as **MoneyTips–YourName** and then close the presentation.
4. Submit the assessment to your instructor in the manner she or he has requested.

◆ **Data Files**   **Assessment 11.5**   ◉   Creating a Self-Running Multimedia Presentation

Type: Individual

Deliverable: Presentation about Yellowstone National Park

1. Create a presentation similar to the one shown below and on the next page in the Assessment 11.5 Yellowstone National Park Presentation with the following additional information:

   a. Theme is *Wood Type*.

   b. Picture and video files are as follows:

Slide 2	**YellowstoneMap**
Slide 3	**OldFaithfulGeyser_nps**
Slide 4	**GreatFountainGeyser**
Slide 5	**InsideYellowstoneVideo**

   c. Use your best judgment to determine other formatting and alignment.

2. Apply transition and animation effects of your choosing, setting up the slide show as a self-running presentation. You determine appropriate times for each slide.

3. Save the presentation in the Ch11 folder within the Assessments folder as **YellowstoneNP-YourName**.

4. Submit the assessment to your instructor in the manner she or he has requested.

5. Close the presentation.

Assessment 11.5
Yellowstone National Park Presentation

continued...

WHERE THE WORLD'S GEYSERS ARE PRESERVED

- ❖ Approximately one-half of the world's hydrothermal features
  - Park has more than 300 geysers
    - Old Faithful, most famous geyser
- ❖ Yellowstone is home to two-thirds of all geysers on earth!

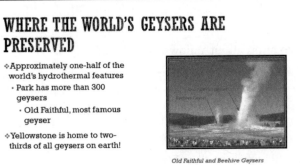

Old Faithful and Beehive Geysers

WHAT IS A GEYSER?

Great Fountain Geyser

- ❖ Hot spring
- ❖ Near surface, constrictions prevent water from moving freely
- ❖ As water rises, steam forms
- ❖ Steam expands as it nears surface and erupts
- ❖ Eruptions can last 1 to 5 minutes
- ❖ Average height of eruption is 145 feet or 44 meters

PREDICTING GEYSER ACTIVITY

Inside
Yellowstone

with

Park Ranger
George Heinz

Assessment 11.5 *(continued)*
Yellowstone National Park Presentation

PHOTO AND VIDEO CREDITS

All photos and video courtesy of:

Yellowstone National Park, National Park Service, US Department of the Interior

To view more multimedia from Yellowstone's Photo Collection, go to
http://www.nps.gov/features/yell/slidefile/index.htm

View
Model Answer
Compare your
completed file with the
model answer.

◆ **Audio File   Assessment 11.6** 🎧 Internet Research and Composing
a New Multimedia Presentation

Type: Individual or Pairs
Deliverable: Presentation about World War II

You have been asked to help the history society celebrate the 75th anniversary of World War II by creating a six to eight slide self-running presentation about the war. These presentations will be loaded on kiosks placed around the school campus. Create your presentation modeled after the World War I presentation in Assessment 11.1 to Assessment 11.3. Find pictures, sound, and a short video clip to enhance the slides and remember to credit the source of all multimedia. The program assistant has left you instructions on voice mail.

1. Listen to the audio file *WorldWarII_Instructions*.
2. Complete the research, locate suitable images and video, and compose the presentation as instructed.
3. Save the presentation in the Ch11 folder within the Assessments folder as **WorldWarII-YourName**.
4. Submit the assessment to your instructor in the manner she or he has requested.
5. Close the presentation.

Assessment 11.7 [N] Sending Assessment Work to OneNote Notebook

Type: Individual
Deliverable: New Page in Shared OneNote notebook

1. Start OneNote and open the MyAssessments notebook created in Chapter 4, Assessment 4.4.
2. Make PowerPoint the active section and add a new page titled *Chapter 11 Assessments*.
3. Switch to PowerPoint. For each assessment that you completed, open the presentation, send the slides formatted as handouts with six slides horizontal per page and with your name in a header to OneNote 2016, selecting the *Chapter 11 Assessments* page in the *PowerPoint* section in the MyAssessments notebook, then close the presentation.
4. Close your MyAssessments notebook in OneNote and then close OneNote.
5. Close PowerPoint.
6. Submit the assessment to your instructor in the manner she or he has requested.

Study Tools

Study Tools

Study tools, including a slide presentation and Quick Steps, are available from this ebook page.

Review Exercises

Review Exercises

Multiple Choice, Matching, and Completion exercises give you an opportunity to review and reinforce your understanding of the material covered in this chapter.

SNAP

If you are a SNAP user, go to your SNAP Assignments page to complete the review exercises.

SNAP Exercises

SNAP

If you are a SNAP user, go to your SNAP Assignments page to complete additional exercises available for you.

Assessments

The following assessments offer opportunities to apply what you have learned in relevant, real-world situations. Save your solution files and URLs, and submit them for evaluation as directed by your instructor.

Data Files

Assessment 12.1 Adding, Editing, and Deleting Records

Type: Individual

Deliverable: Locker Rentals database (continued in all assessments)

1. Open **LockerRentals** and click the Enable Content button in the SECURITY WARNING message bar. If necessary, close the SAVE CHANGES message bar.
2. Use the *Save Database As* option at the Save As backstage area to save a copy of the database named **LockerRentals-YourName** in a new folder named *Ch12* within the Assessments folder on your storage medium.
3. Enable content in the copy of the database.
4. Open the Students table. Add a new record using StudentID *999999999*. Type your first and last names in the appropriate fields and leave all the other fields blank. Close the table.
5. Open the Rentals table. Add the following new record and then close the table when finished.

RentalNumber	Tab past this field as the number is assigned automatically by Access
LockerNumber	Select *A104* in the drop-down list
StudentID	Select *999999999 Your Name* in the drop-down list
DateRented	15sep2018
RentalPaid	Yes
DatePaid	15sep2018

6. Open the Lockers table and then make the following changes to the data:
   a. Change all occurrences of *City Center* to *Downtown Campus*.
   b. Change the level number from *3* to *2* for locker numbers B108, B109, and B110.
   c. Change the locker type from *Box Size* to *Half Size* for locker numbers A101 and A102.
7. Delete the records for locker numbers A106 and C106.
8. Close the Lockers table.
9. Open the Rentals form and then add the following new record:

RentalNumber	Tab past this field as the number is assigned automatically by Access
LockerNumber	Select *A102* in the drop-down list
StudentID	Select *101334799 Su-Lin Cheng* in the drop-down list
DateRented	15sep2018
RentalPaid	Yes
DatePaid	15sep2018

10. Use the Find feature to locate the record in the Locker Rentals form for locker number B100 and then delete the record.
11. Use the Find feature to locate the record in the Locker Rentals form for locker number B106 and then edit the record to show the rental paid on September 16, 2018.
12. Close the Rentals form.
13. Leave the database open if you are continuing to Assessment 12.2; otherwise, close the database and submit the assessment to your instructor in the manner she or he has requested.

Assessment 12.2 Sorting and Filtering Data

Type: Individual
Deliverable: Locker Rentals database and PDF of filtered table (continued from Assessment 12.1)

1. If necessary, open **LockerRentals-YourName** and enable content.
2. Open the Rentals table and then sort the table by *LockerNumber* in ascending order.
3. Close the Rentals table, saving the changes to the table design.
4. Open the Lockers table and then filter the table to show only the Downtown Campus lockers.
5. With the filtered Lockers table active, create a PDF of the table by completing the following steps:
   a. Click the External Data tab.
   b. Click the PDF or XPS button in the Export group.
   c. At the Publish as PDF or XPS dialog box, navigate to the Ch12 folder within Assessments, select the current entry in the *File name* text box, type FilteredLockersTable-YourName, and then click the Publish button.
   d. If necessary, close the PDF window and return to Access.
   e. Close the Export – PDF dialog box that asks if you want to save the export steps.
6. Close the Lockers table. Click No when prompted to save changes to the table design.
7. Leave the database open if you are continuing to Assessment 12.3; otherwise, close the database and submit the assessment to your instructor in the manner she or he has requested.

Assessment 12.3 Creating and Editing Queries

Type: Individual
Deliverable: Locker Rentals database (continued from Assessment 12.2)

1. If necessary, open **LockerRentals-YourName** and enable content.

2. Create a query using the Simple Query Wizard using the following information:
   a. Choose the tables and fields in this order:

Table: Lockers	Add all fields
Table: LockerTypesAndFees	RentalFee

   b. Choose a detail query.
   c. Change the title to *LockerListWithFees*.
3. Switch to Design view for the LockerListWithFees query and then sort the query by the *LockerNumber* field in ascending order.
4. Run the query.
5. Save and close the query.
6. Open the LockerListWithFees query and then switch to Design view.
7. Enter criteria to select the lockers in the Allen Park campus building. Run the query. Use Save Object As to save the revised query as *AllenParkLockers* and then close the query.
8. Open the LockerListWithFees query and then switch to Design view.
9. Enter criteria to select the lockers in the first level only of the Borden Avenue campus building. Run the query. Use Save Object As to save the revised query as *BordenAveL1Lockers* and then close the query.
10. Open the LockerRentals2018 query, switch to Design view, and then delete the *DateRented* column.
11. Insert a new column to the left of the *RentalPaid* column and then type the following formula in the *Field* box:
    Rental Fee with Tax: [RentalFee]*1.05
12. Format the *Rental Fee with Tax* column to Currency.
13. Run the query. Adjust the column width of the calculated column to Best Fit.
14. Save and then close the query.
15. Open the LockerRentals2018 query. Switch to Design view. Enter criteria to select only those records where the rental fee has been paid. Run the query. Use Save Object As to save the revised query as *PaidLockerRentals2018* and then close the query.
16. Leave the database open if you are continuing to Assessment 12.4; otherwise, close the database and submit the assessment to your instructor in the manner she or he has requested.

Assessment 12.4 Previewing and Creating PDFs of Database Objects

Type: Individual
Deliverable: PDFs of tables and queries in Locker Rentals database (continued from Assessment 12.3)

1. If necessary, open **LockerRentals-YourName** and enable content.
2. Open the Lockers table and then display the table in the Print Preview window.
3. Click the PDF or XPS button in the Data group on the Print Preview tab. At the Publish as PDF or XPS dialog box, navigate to the Ch12 folder within Assessments and publish a PDF of the table, naming it **LockersTable-YourName**. If necessary, close the PDF window and return to Access. Close the Export – PDF dialog box.
4. Close the Print Preview window and then close the Lockers table.
5. Complete steps similar to Steps 2 to 4 to create a PDF for each of the following objects, changing the file names as noted.
   Note: Consider clearing the Open file after publishing *check box in the Publish as PDF or XPS dialog box if the box is checked.*

Object Name	Name for PDF
Rentals table	RentalsTable-YourName
AllenParkLockers	AllenParkLockers-YourName
BordenAveL1Lockers	BordenAveL1Lockers-YourName
LockerListWithFees	LockerListWithFees-YourName

6. Create a PDF for each of the following queries by completing steps similar to Steps 2 to 4, changing the page layout to landscape orientation and the margins to *Normal*.

Object Name   Name for PDF
LockerRentals2018   LockerRentals2018-YourName
PaidLockerRentals2018   PaidLockerRentals2018-YourName

7. Leave the database open if you are continuing to Assessment 12.5; otherwise, close the database and submit the assessment to your instructor in the manner she or he has requested.

Assessment 12.5 Visual—Modifying a Query to Add Criteria and a Calculation

Type: Individual

Deliverable: PDF of query with calculated field (continued from Assessment 12.4)

1. If necessary, open **LockerRentals-Your Name** and enable content.
2. Open the LockerListWithFees query and modify the query to create the query results datasheet shown below in the Assessment 12.5 Query with Criteria and Calculated Column datasheet. You determine the required calculated column *Field* expression as well as the criteria used to generate the query results datasheet. **Hint:** *The rental fee is for eight months*. Best Fit the calculated column width.
3. Create a PDF of the query, naming it **AllenParkAndBordenAveLockers-YourName** and saving it in the Ch12 folder within the Assessments folder. Make sure the datasheet fits on one page.
4. Use Save Object As to save the revised query as *AllenParkAndBordenAveLockers*, close the query saving changes to the design, and then close the LockerRentals database.
5. Submit the assessment to your instructor in the manner she or he has requested.

AllenParkAndBordenAveLockers					
LockerNumber	LockerType	CampusBuilding	Level	RentalFee	Rental Fee Per Month
A101	Half size	Allen Park	1	$70.00	$8.75
A102	Half size	Allen Park	1	$70.00	$8.75
A103	Full Size Regular	Allen Park	1	$80.00	$10.00
A104	Full Size Regular	Allen Park	1	$80.00	$10.00
A105	Half size	Allen Park	1	$70.00	$8.75
A107	Full Size Regular	Allen Park	2	$80.00	$10.00
A108	Full Size Regular	Allen Park	2	$80.00	$10.00
A109	Full Size Wide	Allen Park	2	$95.00	$11.88
A110	Full Size Wide	Allen Park	2	$95.00	$11.88
A115	Full Size Regular	Allen Park	2	$80.00	$10.00
A120	Full Size Regular	Allen Park	2	$80.00	$10.00
B100	Full Size Regular	Borden Avenue	1	$80.00	$10.00
B101	Box Size	Borden Avenue	1	$65.00	$8.13
B102	Box Size	Borden Avenue	1	$65.00	$8.13
B103	Full Size Regular	Borden Avenue	1	$80.00	$10.00
B104	Full Size Wide	Borden Avenue	1	$95.00	$11.88
B105	Full Size Wide	Borden Avenue	1	$95.00	$11.88
B106	Full Size Regular	Borden Avenue	1	$80.00	$10.00
B107	Box Size	Borden Avenue	1	$65.00	$8.13
B108	Full Size Wide	Borden Avenue	2	$95.00	$11.88
B109	Full Size Wide	Borden Avenue	2	$95.00	$11.88
B110	Box Size	Borden Avenue	2	$65.00	$8.13

Assessment 12.5 Query with Criteria and Calculated Column

View
Model Answer
Compare your completed file with the model answer.

Assessment 12.6 Ⓝ OneNote—Sending Assessment Work to OneNote Notebook

Type: Individual

Deliverable: New page in Shared OneNote notebook

1. Start OneNote and open the MyAssessments notebook created in Chapter 4, Assessment 4.4.
2. Make Access the active section and add a new page titled *Chapter 12 Assessments*.
3. For each PDF you created in an assessment in this chapter, send the PDF to OneNote 2016, selecting the Chapter 12 Assessments page in the Access section in the MyAssessments notebook. If you completed all assessments, insert the PDFs on the OneNote page in this order:
   FilteredLockersTable-YourName
   LockersTable-YourName
   RentalsTable-YourName
   AllenParkLockers-YourName
   BordenAveL1Lockers-YourName
   LockerListWithFees-YourName
   LockerRentals2018-YourName
   PaidLockerRentals2018-YourName
   AllenParkAndBordenAveLockers-YourName
4. Close your MyAssessments notebook in OneNote and then close OneNote.
5. Submit the assessment to your instructor in the manner she or he has requested.

Study Tools

Study tools, including a slide presentation and Quick Steps, are available from this ebook page.

Review Exercises

Multiple Choice, Matching, and Completion exercises give you an opportunity to review and reinforce your understanding of the material covered in this chapter.

If you are a SNAP user, go to your SNAP Assignments page to complete the review exercises.

SNAP Exercises

If you are a SNAP user, go to your SNAP Assignments page to complete additional exercises available for you.

Assessments

The following assessments offer opportunities to apply what you have learned in relevant, real-world situations. Save your solution files and URLs, and submit them for evaluation as directed by your instructor.

Assessment 13.1 Creating a New Database File and Creating Tables

Type: Individual

Deliverable: Home listing database (continued in Assessment 13.2)

1. Create a new blank desktop database file named ***Listings-YourName*** in a new folder named *C13* in the Assessments folder on your storage medium.
2. Add the following fields in the blank *Table1* datasheet in addition to the default *ID* field:

Field Name	Data Type	Caption
SoldDate	Date & Time	Date Sold
SalePrice	Currency	Sale Price
Commission	Number	Commission Rate
SellingAgent	Short Text	Selling Agent

3. Adjust column widths so that all column headings are entirely visible.
4. Save the table as *Sales* and then close the table.
5. Create a new table in Design view using the following field names and data types:

Field Name	Data Type
ListingID	Short Text
AgentID	Short Text
StreetAdd	Short Text
ClientLName	Short Text
ClientFName	Short Text
ListDate	Date/Time
AskPrice	Currency
HomeType	Short Text

6. Assign *ListingID* as the primary key field.

7. Save the table naming it *Listings* and then close the table.
8. Create a third table in the database using the following field names. All the fields are the Short Text data type. You decide the view in which to create the table.
   Field Name
   AgentID (assign this field as the primary key)
   LName
   FName
9. Save the table as *Agents* and then close the table.
10. Leave the database open if you are continuing to Assessment 13.2; otherwise, close the database and submit the assessment to your instructor in the manner she or he has requested.

Assessment 13.2 Adding Fields, Modifying Field Properties, and Creating a Lookup List

Type: Individual
Deliverable: Home listing database and PDFs of tables (continued from Assessment 13.1)

1. If necessary, open **Listings-YourName** and enable content.
2. Open the Listings table, make *ClientFName* the active field, and add a new Short Text field named *ContactPhone*.
3. Switch to Design view and then create a drop-down list for the *HomeType* field with the following list entries. Make *Single family home* the default value for the field.
   Single family home
   Condominium
   Townhouse
   Duplex
   Triplex
   Fourplex
   Other
4. Save the table and then switch to Datasheet view. Adjust the column widths as needed so that all column headings and the default value for the *HomeType* field are entirely visible, and then close the table saving changes to the layout.
5. Open the Sales table and then add a new Yes/No field named *SplitComm* to the end of the table. Add a caption to the field with the text *Split Commission?* and then adjust the column width to show the entire column heading.
6. Switch to Design view, make *Commission* the active field, and then change the following field properties:
   a. Type *.05* as the Default Value.
   b. Change the Field Size to *Double*.
   c. Change the Decimal Places to *2*.
   d. Change the Format to *Percent*.
7. Change the field name of the *ID* field to *ListingID* and then change the data type from *AutoNumber* to *Short Text*.
8. Save and close the Sales table.
9. Add the following captions to the fields in the Agents table and then adjust column widths in Datasheet view so that all column headings are entirely visible. Close the table, saving changes to the layout.

Field Name	Caption
AgentID	Agent ID
LName	Agent Last Name
FName	Agent First Name

10. Add a new record in the Agents table with your name and with *10* as the *AgentID*.

11. Add the following record in the Listings table:

ListingID	2018-1	*ContactPhone*	800-555-3225
AgentID	10	*ListDate*	03/15/2018
StreetAdd	98 First Street	*AskPrice*	87500
ClientLName	Jones	*HomeType*	Condominium
ClientFName	Marion		

12. Add the following new record to the Sales table:

ListingID	2018-1	*Commission Rate*	5.00%
Date Sold	03/22/2018	*SellingAgent*	10
Sale Price	82775	*Split Commission?*	Yes

13. Display each table datasheet in Print Preview and then create a PDF of the datasheet using the following file names and saving in the Ch13 folder in Assessments:

Table	Name for PDF
Agents	Agents-Your Name
Listings (landscape; normal margins)	Listings-Your Name
Sales (normal margins)	Sales-Your Name

14. Close the **Listings-YourName** database.
15. Submit the assessment to your instructor in the manner she or he has requested.

◆ **Data Files** **Assessment 13.3** Editing Relationships, Creating a Form and a Report

Type: Individual
Deliverable: Home listing database and PDFs of new objects (continued in Assessments 13.4 and 13.5)

1. Open **HomeListings**.
2. Use Save As to *Save Database As*, naming the copy **HomeListings-YourName** in the Ch13 folder within the Assessments folder on your storage medium.
3. Enable content in the copy of the database.
4. Display the relationships.
5. Edit each relationship to turn on *Enforce Referential Integrity*. With the relationships window still open, capture an image of your screen and paste the image into a new Word document. Save the Word document as **Relationships-YourName** and save it in the Ch13 folder in Assessments. Close Word and then close the Relationships window.
6. Create a form using the Form tool for the Listings table and then modify the form as follows:
   a. Change to a theme of your choosing.
   b. Insert the picture named *ForSale*. Change the Size Mode property to *Zoom*, the *Width* to 1.5 inches, and the *Height* to 1 inch.
   c. Change the font size for the title text to a size of your choosing.
   d. Make any other changes you think improve the appearance of the form.
   e. Save the form using the default form name and then close the form.
7. Reopen the form and then display the first page in Print Preview. Change the margins to *Normal*. Open the Page Setup dialog box and then click the Columns tab. Change the *Width* in the *Column Size* section to 7.5 inches and then click OK. Create a PDF of the *first page only* of the form, naming the PDF **ListingsForm-YourName** and saving it in the Ch13 folder in Assessments. *Hint: Use the Options button in the Publish as PDF or XPS dialog box to choose Page(s) 1 to 1 before clicking the Publish button.* Close the form, saving changes if prompted to save the form.
8. Create a report using the Report tool for the Sales table and then modify the report as follows:
   a. Insert the **ForSale** picture, applying the same changes as those applied to the picture in the form.
   b. Change the title text to a font size of your choosing.

c. Resize controls as needed so that all objects fit on one page.

d. Select and then delete the total and the line above the total at the bottom of the *Sale Price* column.

e. Make any other changes you think will improve the appearance of the report.

f. Save the report using the default report name.

9. Create a PDF of the report, naming it **SalesReport-YourName** and saving it in the Ch13 folder in Assessments. Close the report.

10. Leave the database open if you are continuing to Assessment 13.4; otherwise, close the database and submit the assessment to your instructor in the manner she or he has requested.

Assessment 13.4 Compacting on Close and Backing Up a Database

Type: Individual

Deliverable: Home listing database (continued from Assessment 13.3 and continues in Assessment 13.5)

1. If necessary, open **HomeListings-YourName** and enable content.

2. Turn on the *Compact on Close* option for the database.

3. Create a backup copy of the database, accepting the default file name and saving in the default folder.

4. Leave the database open if you are continuing to Assessment 13.5; otherwise, close the database and submit the assessment to your instructor in the manner she or he has requested.

Assessment 13.5 👁 Visual—Creating a Query and Report

Type: Individual

Deliverable: PDF of Report (continued from Assessment 13.4)

1. If necessary, open **HomeListings-YourName** and enable content.

2. Create a query using all the fields in the Sales table. Insert a calculated column titled *Amount* between *Commission Rate* and *Selling Agent* as shown in the Assessment 13.5 Sales Commissions report below. You determine the field expression and format. Save the query, naming it **SalesCommissions**. Close the query.

3. Create a report similar to the Assessment 13.5 Sales Commissions report shown below, based on the SalesCommissions query. Use your best judgment to determine the formatting options by examining Assessment 13.5 and by exploring the four Report Layout Tools tabs. Save the report using the default name.

Sales Commissions

ListingID	Date Sold	Sale Price	Commission Rate	Amount	Selling Agent	Split Commission?
2018-1	3/22/2018	$82,775.00	5.00%	$4,138.75	Student last name	☑
2018-3	3/31/2018	$59,000.00	4.00%	$2,360.00	Davidson	☑
2018-4	3/30/2018	$72,000.00	5.00%	$3,600.00	Polaski	☑
2018-7	3/31/2018	$74,500.00	5.00%	$3,725.00	Ungar	☑
2018-9	3/25/2018	$64,500.00	5.00%	$3,225.00	Antoine	☑

View
Model Answer
Compare your completed file with the model answer.

Assessment 13.5 Sales Commissions report

4. Open the Page Setup dialog box with the Columns tab active. Check the *Width* in the *Column Size* section and change the *Width* to 8 inches if necessary. Create a PDF of the report in portrait orientation and with narrow margins, saving it as **SalesCommissions–YourName** in the Ch13 folder within Assessments.
5. Close the report and then close the database.
6. Submit the assessment to your instructor in the manner she or he has requested.

Assessment 13.6 N Sending Assessment Work to OneNote Notebook

Type: Individual
Deliverable: New Page in Shared OneNote notebook

1. Start OneNote and open the MyAssessments notebook created in Chapter 4, Assessment 4.4.
2. Make Access the active section and add a new page titled *Chapter 13 Assessments*.
3. For each PDF you created in an assessment you completed in this chapter, send the PDF to OneNote 2016, selecting the Chapter 13 Assessments page in the Access section in the MyAssessments notebook.
   If you completed all assessments, insert the PDFs on the OneNote page in this order:
   Agents–YourName
   Listings–YourName
   Sales–YourName
   Relationships–YourName
   ListingsForm–YourName
   SalesReport–YourName
   SalesCommissions–YourName
4. Close your MyAssessments notebook in OneNote and then close OneNote.
5. Submit the assessment to your instructor in the manner she or he has requested.

Study Tools

**Study Tools**   Study tools, including a slide presentation and Quick Steps, are available from this ebook page.

Review Exercises

**Review Exercises**   Multiple Choice, Matching, and Completion exercises give you an opportunity to review and reinforce your understanding of the material covered in this chapter.

SNAP   If you are a SNAP user, go to your SNAP Assignments page to complete the review exercises.

SNAP Exercises

SNAP   If you are a SNAP user, go to your SNAP Assignments page to complete additional exercises available for you.

Assessments

The following assessments offer opportunities to apply what you have learned in relevant, real-world situations. Save your solution files and URLs, and submit them for evaluation as directed by your instructor.

**Data Files**   ### Assessment 14.1 Importing and Exporting Data with Access and Excel

Type: Individual
Deliverable: Database and worksheet with used books list

1. Start Access and then open the **UsedBooks** database.
2. Use Save As to save a copy of the database as **UsedBooks-YourName** in a new folder *Ch14* within Assessments.
3. Enable Content in the copy of the database.
4. Import the Excel workbook named ***BookList*** from the Ch14 folder in Student_ Data_Files using the option *Append a copy of the records to the table* [Books] at the Get External Data – Excel Spreadsheet dialog box. Do not save the import steps. ***Note:*** *Only two dialog boxes are required in the Import Spreadsheet Wizard when you use the Append option.*
5. Open the Books table when the import is complete, review the datasheet, and then close the table.
6. Create a query in Design view adding the Books table and the Students table to the query and with the following fields in order:

Field Name	Table Name
BookID	Books
FName	Students
LName	Students
Title	Books
Author	Books
Condition	Books
AskPrice	Books
StopPrice	Books

7. Save the query as **BookList** and then run the query.
8. Review the query results datasheet and then close the query.
9. Export the BookList query to Excel, saving the workbook as **ExportedBookList-YourName** in the Ch14 folder within Assessments. Select the options to export data with formatting and layout information and to open the destination when the export is complete. Do not save the export steps.
10. Make the following changes to the worksheet in Excel:
    a. Change each occurrence of *Jane Doe* to your first and last names in the *First Name* and *Last Name* columns.
    b. Change the orientation to *Landscape*.
    c. Make sure all columns will fit on one page.
    d. Create a header with the sheet tab name at the top center of the page and a footer with your name at the bottom center of the page.
11. Save the revised workbook using the same name (**ExportedBookList-YourName**) and then close Excel.
12. Close the database and then close Access.
13. Submit the assessment to your instructor in the manner she or he has requested.

◆ **Data Files**   **Assessment 14.2** Embedding Data with Word and Excel

Type: Individual
Deliverable: Document with embedded tables from Excel

1. Start Word and then open **StatCounterTables**.
2. Use Save As to change the file name to **StatCounterTables-YourName**, saving in the Ch14 folder within Assessments.
3. Start Excel and then open **SocialMediaStats**.
4. Select and copy A4:B11.
5. Switch to Word and position the insertion point at the left margin a double-space below the first paragraph. Use *Paste Special* from the Paste button arrow to open the Paste Special dialog box. Select *Microsoft Excel Worksheet Object* in the *As* list box and then choose OK to embed the worksheet data.
6. Center the embedded worksheet object.
7. Embed C4:D11 from the Excel worksheet, inserting the object a double-space below the last paragraph in the document.
8. Center the embedded worksheet object.
9. Edit both embedded objects to display two decimal places after each percent value.
    Hint: Before ending editing of each embedded object, make sure the cells displayed in the editing window are only the cells that were copied.
10. Add your name in a footer in the document.
11. Save the revised document using the same name (**StatCounterTables-YourName**) and then close Word.
12. Close Excel. Click Don't Save if prompted to save changes to the worksheet when closing Excel.
13. Submit the assessment to your instructor in the manner she or he has requested.

**Data Files   Assessment 14.3** Linking Data between Word and Excel

Type: Individual
Deliverable: Document with linked Excel charts

1. Start Word and then open **StatCounterCharts**.
2. Use Save As to change the file name to **LinkedStatCounterCharts-YourName**, saving in the Ch14 folder within Assessments.
3. Start Excel and then open **SocialMediaStats**.
4. Use Save As to change the file name to **LinkedSocialMediaStats-YourName**, saving in the Ch14 folder within Assessments.
5. Select, copy, and link the *Global Market Share* pie chart to the Word document a double-space below the first paragraph. Select the option to link using the destination theme. Center the chart in the document.
6. Select, copy, and link the *United States Market Share* pie chart to the Word document a double-space below the last paragraph. Select the option to link using the destination theme. Center the chart in the document.
7. Turn on the option for each linked object to automatically update.
8. Add your name in a footer in the document.
9. Save the revised document using the same name (**LinkedStatCounterCharts-YourName**) and then close the document.
10. Make the following changes to the data in the Excel worksheet:

Cell Address	Current Entry	New Entry
B5	71.7	60.4
D5	60.1	45.8
A6	StumbleUpon	Instagram
B6	1.5	12.8
C6	StumbleUpon	Instagram
D6	3.4	17.7

11. Save the revised workbook using the same name (**LinkedSocialMediaStats-YourName**) and then close Excel.
12. With Word active, open **LinkedStatCounterCharts-YourName** and choose Yes when prompted to update links. Save and then close the document after updating links and exit Word.
13. Submit the assessment to your instructor in the manner she or he has requested.

Data Files   Assessment 14.4 👁 Embedding Excel Data in PowerPoint

Type: Individual
Deliverable: PowerPoint presentation with embedded Excel data

1. Start PowerPoint and then open **TopVacDestinations**.
2. Modify the presentation to resemble the one shown in the Assessment 14.4 Vacation Destinations Survey Results presentation on the next page, using the following information:
   a. The tables on slide 2 and slide 3 are embedded from the Excel worksheet named **VacDestinations**.
   b. Edit the embedded objects to appear as shown in the Assessment 14.4 presentation. Use your best judgment to match colors and borders.
   c. Add slide 4 as a new slide.
   d. Add the image shown on the title slide by searching in Online Pictures using the keyword *luggage*, or by inserting the student data file named **luggage**.
3. Save the revised presentation as **TopVacDestinations-YourName**.
4. Close PowerPoint and Excel.
5. Submit the assessment to your instructor in the manner she or he has requested.

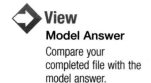

View

Model Answer

Compare your completed file with the model answer.

Top Vacation Destinations

Western Hiker Association

This Year's Online Survey Results

Worldwide Destinations

Destination	Percent
London	32
Barcelona	13
Paris	14
Edinburgh	11
Zurich	10
Crete	10
Beijing	11

United States and Canada Destinations

Destination	Percent
Maui	18
San Francisco	24
New Orleans	11
Vancouver	9
Charleston	16
Banff	14
Montreal	9

Assessment 14.4 Vacation Destinations Survey Results presentation

Next Year's Survey

- Survey planning starts next month
- Survey opens early in January
- Results to be reported by December 31
- Expecting new destinations to appear from South America

Assessment 14.5 [N] Sending Assessment Work to OneNote Notebook

Type: Individual

Deliverable: New Page in Shared OneNote notebook

1. Start OneNote and then open the MyAssessments notebook created in Chapter 4, Assessment 4.4.
2. Make Integrating the active section and then add a new page titled *Chapter 14 Assessments*.
3. Send the following documents to OneNote selecting the Chapter 14 Assessments page in the Integrating section in the MyAssessments notebook. Skip any assessments you were not assigned to complete.
   a. **ExportedBookList–YourName** from Excel.
   b. **StatCounterTables–YourName** from Word.
   c. **LinkedStatCounterCharts–YourName** from Word. Choose No when prompted to update links when you reopen this file.
   d. **TopVacDestinations–YourName** from PowerPoint. Send the slides formatted as handouts with four slides horizontal per page and with your name in a header. Save the changes when prompted when the file is closed.
4. Close your MyAssessments notebook in OneNote and then close OneNote.
5. Submit the assessment to your instructor in the manner she or he has requested.

Study Tools

Study Tools Study tools, including a slide presentation and Quick Steps, are available from this ebook page.

Review Exercises

Review Exercises Multiple Choice, Matching, and Completion exercises give you an opportunity to review and reinforce your understanding of the material covered in this chapter.

If you are a SNAP user, go to your SNAP Assignments page to complete the review exercises.

SNAP Exercises

If you are a SNAP user, go to your SNAP Assignments page to complete additional exercises available for you.

Assessments

The following assessments offer opportunities to apply what you have learned in relevant, real-world situations. Save your solution files and URLs, and submit them for evaluation as directed by your instructor.

Assessment 15.1 Creating a Document with Word Online

Type: Individual
Deliverable: Document in OneDrive

1. Open a browser window and sign in to OneDrive.
2. Start a new blank document in Word Online and then type the following text using the default settings.

What Is Office 365?

Office 365 is the subscription-based model for purchasing Office 2016. An Office 365 Home subscription offers home users Office 2016 applications from the cloud for up to five PCs or Macs for $10 per month. At OneDrive, registered users have access to web-based editions for Word, Excel, PowerPoint, Outlook, and OneNote. According to Microsoft, these are the additional benefits included with an Office 365 subscription:

- desktop applications for Publisher and Access
- 1 TB storage each for up to five users
- 60 Skype world minutes per month each for up to five users

Because Office 365 is hosted by Microsoft as a cloud computing technology, the software will always be up to date and accessible from any device with an Internet connection. Office 365 is ideal for consumers with multiple devices who want to view or edit documents from any location at any time.

Purchasing an Office 365 subscription is an option that home users may want to consider. Keep in mind that to continue using the software, the subscription fee must be paid monthly. Whether the cost will be less expensive over the long run depends on the number of traditional software licenses you would buy and whether you upgrade immediately to new releases. Finally, consider if you need the additional options that the subscription is offering. For example, if you do not use Access, Publisher, or Skype, the additional benefits are not meaningful to you.

3. Perform a spelling check and carefully proofread the document.
4. Apply formatting options of your choosing to improve the appearance of the document.
5. Search for and insert a suitable picture at the bottom center of the document.
6. Rename the document **Office365-YourName**.
7. Close the document tab.
8. Submit the assessment to your instructor in the manner she or he has requested.

Assessment 15.2 Creating a Worksheet in Excel Online

Type: Individual
Deliverable: Workbook in OneDrive

1. With OneDrive open, start a new blank workbook in Excel Online and then set up the following information in a worksheet. You determine the worksheet layout.

Cost Comparison for Office 365 and Office 2016 Subscription fee versus standard software license for each PC			
Office 365 Home		Office 2016 Desktop PC	
Monthly subscription fee	10	Office 2016 Home and Student license fee	139.00
Estimated years to subscribe	4	Number of licenses to buy	3
TOTAL COST FOR OFFICE 365		TOTAL COST FOR OFFICE 2016	
Difference in cost Office 365 versus Office 2016 Desktop licensing			

2. Create formulas to calculate the total cost of Office 365, the total cost of Office 2016, and the difference between the two models.
3. Apply formatting options of your choosing to improve the appearance of the worksheet.
4. Rename the workbook **Office365CostComparison-YourName** and then close the workbook tab.
5. Submit the assessment to your instructor in the manner she or he has requested.

Assessment 15.3 Creating a Presentation in PowerPoint Online

Type: Individual
Deliverable: Presentation in OneDrive

1. With OneDrive open, start a new blank presentation in PowerPoint Online.
2. Select a theme and variant of your choosing.
3. On Slide 1 type What Is Office 365 Home? as the slide title and your name as the subtitle.
4. Add a minimum of two slides to the presentation with text that you compose that summarizes the main points from the text that you typed in Assessment 15. For example, in Slide 2 explain the cloud-based subscription model of purchasing Office 365, and in Slide 3 provide a list of what is included in an Office 365 Home subscription.
5. Apply formatting options of your choosing to enhance the presentation.
6. Rename the presentation **Office365Pres-YourName** and then close the presentation tab.
7. Submit the assessment to your instructor in the manner she or he has requested.

Assessment 15.4 Download Assessment Files and File Management in OneDrive

Type: Individual

Deliverable: Downloaded assessment files on a storage medium; Word document with screen images of file lists in OneDrive

1. With OneDrive open, select and download **Office365–YourName**.
2. Select and download **Office365CostComparison–YourName**.
3. Select and download **Office365Pres–YourName**.
4. Use File Explorer to create a new folder *Ch15* within Assessments on your storage medium and then copy and paste the three files downloaded from OneDrive in Steps 1 through 3 into the new folder. Close the File Explorer window when finished.
5. In OneDrive and with *Files > Documents* displayed in the Content pane, click <u>New</u> in the bar along the top of the window and then click <u>Folder</u>. Create a new folder *C15-Assessments* within Documents.
6. Select and move the files created from Assessments 15.1, 15.2, and 15.3 to the C15-Assessments folder.
7. With *Files > Documents* the active list displayed in OneDrive, create another new folder *C15-Topics*.
8. Select and move the three files created from the topics in this chapter to the C15-Topics folder.
9. Capture an image of your desktop with *Files > Documents* active in your OneDrive account. Start a new Word document using the desktop edition (not Word Online) and paste the image.
10. Switch back to OneDrive, click the C15-Assessments folder tile, and then capture an image of your desktop with the folder contents displayed. Paste the image into the Word document below the capture pasted at Step 9.
11. Switch back to OneDrive and display *Files > Documents* in the content pane, then click the C15-Topics folder tile. Capture an image of your desktop with the folder contents displayed and paste the image into the Word document below the capture pasted at Step 10.
12. Save the Word document as **OneDriveFiles–YourName** in the Ch15 folder within Assessments on your storage medium and then close Word.
13. Sign out of OneDrive.
14. Submit the assessment to your instructor in the manner she or he has requested.

Assessment 15.5 👁 Visual—Creating a Spreadsheet in Google Sheets

Type: Individual

Deliverable: Downloaded copy of Google Sheets spreadsheet and Google Docs document

1. Sign in to Google Drive and use Google Sheets to create the **Assessment 15.5 Cloud Computing Storage Options** spreadsheet on the next page.
2. Rename the spreadsheet as **CloudStorageCosts–YourName**.
3. Use your best judgment to determine font size and shading color for cells.
4. When the spreadsheet is completed, complete the following steps to download a copy of the Google Sheets spreadsheet and the Google Docs document created in Topic 15.7.
   a. At Google Drive, click to select the CloudStorageCosts-YourName thumbnail.
   b. Click the More button located at the right end of the Drive bar. The button displays with three vertical dots and is located next to the trash can. Click <u>Download</u> at the drop-down list.
   c. Next, select and download the file for the document created in Topic 15.7 by following steps similar to those in Steps 4a to 4b.

5. Open a File Explorer window and copy **CloudStorageCosts–YourName** from the Downloads folder to the Ch15 folder within Assessments on your storage medium. Next, copy the **CloudComputing–YourName** document from the Downloads folder to the Ch15 folder within CompletedTopicsByChapter on your storage medium. Close the File Explorer window.
6. Sign out of Google Drive and close the browser window.
7. Submit the assessment to your instructor in the manner she or he has requested.

	A	B	C	D	E
1	**Cloud Computing Storage Options**				
2	**Survey of Five Cloud Storage Service Providers**				
3	**Service Provider**	**Free storage (GB)**	**Upgrade storage (GB)**	**Annual upgrade fee**	**File size limit (GB)**
4	Microsoft OneDrive	15	100	$24	10
5	Google Drive	15	100	$24	10
6	Dropbox	2	100	$120	10
7	Box	10	100	$120	5
8	Amazon Cloud Drive	15	250	$60	None

Assessment 15.5 *Cloud Computing Storage Options* **spreadsheet in Google Sheets**

View
Model Answer
Compare your completed file with the model answer.

Assessment 15.6 [N] OneNote—Sending Assessment Work to OneNote Notebook

Type: Individual
Deliverable: New Page in shared OneNote notebook

1. Start OneNote and open the MyAssessments notebook created in Chapter 4, Assessment 4.4.
2. Make CloudTech the active section and then add a new page titled *Chapter 15 Assessments*.
3. Send the following assessment documents to OneNote, selecting the Chapter 15 Assessments page in the CloudTech section in the MyAssessments notebook. For each assessment, open the file downloaded from OneDrive in the desktop version of the software to send the file to OneNote. Skip any assessments you were not assigned to complete.
   a. **Office365–YourName** from Word.
   b. **Office365CostComparison–YourName** from Excel.
   c. **Office365Pres–YourName** from PowerPoint. Send the slides formatted as handouts with four slides horizontal per page and with your name in a header.
   d. **OneDriveFiles–YourName** from Word.
   e. **CloudStorageCosts–YourName** from Excel.
4. Close your MyAssessments notebook in OneNote and then close OneNote.
5. Submit the assessment to your instructor in the manner she or he has requested.